Boost Your Sex Life

A Erotic Hypnosis Beginners Guide & 7 hours of redy-to-use Femdom Scripts (3-in-1 Collection)

By
Alexandra Morris

Table of Contents

Book Three

Introduction: What is Erotic Hypnosis?

Erotic Hypnosis is the induction of a state of consciousness during which a person becomes highly open to suggestions for the purposes of sexual satisfaction. Now you're probably asking yourself, *"What on Earth does any of that mean?"* so let us break it down into its elements. To gain the most from this book, it is critical you enter with a complete and comprehensive understanding of erotic hypnosis.

Most of us *think* we understand what hypnosis is, but the popular cultural perception is wildly different from the actual practice. Hypnosis is not about mind control or performance art. It's not about tricking people into embarrassing behaviors or uncovering lost memories. Hypnosis is simply a form of therapy that can be used recreationally or clinically. As a respected author, I feel it is important for you to have all the facts. Any claims made in this book will be based on reality. By giving you accurate and pertinent information, your expectations will be accurate as well.

What this book does give you is a beginner's crash course for performing recreational hypnosis safely and effectively. Just because you didn't achieve the 250 coursework hours necessary to be a certified hypnotherapist doesn't mean you and your partner can't benefit from understanding the fundamental principles of hypnosis. Much like how you don't need a degree in kinesiology to learn to run or lift weights, you don't need to be a certified hypnotherapist to benefit from understanding the practice.

If practiced and performed properly, erotic hypnosis will open an entirely new world of sexual satisfaction for you. More and more people are coming to erotic hypnosis for a myriad of reasons. Some people see the intrinsic Dominant/submissive dynamic in hypnosis and want to apply it to their own sexual relationships. Others enjoy the thought of relinquishing control, while others need an elaborate organization of kinks and rituals to perform at all.

The Benefits of Erotic Hypnosis

The Benefits of erotic hypnosis are many; hence, the entire book you're holding. When all safety precautions are followed, there is no wrong way to enjoy erotic hypnosis. Some people find it incredibly difficult to enjoy sex. Sex should be about love, passion, pleasure, exploration, and devotion, but some people find those things terrifying. It's so strange to think how long humans have been having sex (literally since humans existed) and how we got it all twisted it up to a point many of us find it difficult to enjoy.

Stop me if any of these things have ever happened to you. You work all day, get home and immediately have to cook, clean, run errands, shuttle the kids somewhere, negotiate some bill on the phone, go grocery shopping, meet a client or family member, and by the time you get to bed, sex is the last thing on your mind. It literally happens to all of us. Stress and exhaustion are a deadly cocktail when it comes to your libido. Stress can literally inhibit sexual arousal and sexual response to the point of erectile dysfunction. In fact, studies indicate stress and anxiety are the leading

3

cause of sexual dysfunction! That just goes to show how much of an effect our mentality and consciousness can have on the machinations of our bodies.

It might not even be daily stress that makes sex difficult for us to enjoy. If you have a history of trauma that can be sexual and/or emotional, if you grew up in a shame-based religious household, or if your culture shames the idea of a woman having a sexual appetite, it can be extremely difficult if not impossible to enjoy sex. Fortunately, there are solutions. When dealing with people who have suffered trauma, it is extremely important to take every precaution possible and consult with a licensed therapist about your intentions.

No one can guarantee any form of therapy will have the desired results. Any specialist, book, or treatment program that promises results is lying. Every one of us is unique, and our minds and bodies will respond to things differently. What I can guarantee is results are possible. Many people have found intense and repeatable sexual satisfaction from erotic hypnosis. There is a relief for people who suffer from psychological, sexual dysfunction. Hypnosis is simply one of many tools that can be used to treat it, and it is an effective, non-invasive tool at that.

As far as femdom erotic hypnosis goes, some men may find it difficult to submit to another person, especially a woman. This is simply the nature of almost every human culture on Earth but is also the reason why so many men find female domination so tantalizing. It is a power balance so unique in human culture it borders on taboo. Some men will find hypnotic suggestion opens them up to the possibility of female domination or beginning a female-led relationship.

And if you can't find sexual satisfaction from hypnosis, you can still use the techniques in this book for mindfulness, guided meditation, self-awareness, and relaxation. Hypnosis is extremely close to meditation and is arguably a form of guided meditation with a narrow set of rules and intentions. There are many benefits to erotic hypnosis, and ironically the most important thing for you to do above all else is to keep an open mind.

Chapter One: Female Domination aka Femdom

Now that we have a strong understanding of what hypnosis is and what you can hope to achieve with it in a sexual capacity let us now look towards female domination for a comprehensive understanding of femdom erotic hypnosis.

Domination and submission are two complementary roles sexual partners can undertake for the purposes of power exchange during sex. The Dominant is the active force in a relationship, controlling their partner to various limits, which are understood and agreed upon beforehand. A submissive relinquishes a portion of their control to their Dominant for the purposes of sexual and emotional satisfaction. These roles can apply outside the bedroom as well, but for the purposes of femdom erotic hypnosis, we will only discuss them in a sexual capacity. Bear in mind anyone can be a Dominant, submissive, or a switch, which means they swap between the two roles day-to-day, week-to-week, or even moment-to-moment in the same session.

Why would someone want to be Dominant or submissive? There are many reasons why someone would choose either or both roles. For those who experience anxiety, allowing others to make decisions for them or who may feel powerless outside the bedroom, being a Dominant allows them to assume a role where they have greater control over their circumstances than would usually be allotted to them. Bear in mind a Dominant only has as much control as their submissive cedes to them, and all limits and desires should be discussed beforehand. Many women gravitate to the role of Dominant because their personal life and/or culture doesn't afford them the level of power and agency they desire.

While being a Dominant seems to have instant appeal to most people (who wouldn't want to have more power and control of their lives?), there is also a large subset of people who desire no control or agency whatsoever. Some people feel great anxiety when circumstances are beyond their control. Submissives, on the other hand, feel great anxiety when they have too much power in a situation. If you have trouble making important decisions, telling people what to do, or sticking up for yourself, then you may be a submissive. During sex, a submissive relinquishes power to their Dominant and relishes in the joy and freedom of losing control to another person. Free of decision anxiety and the onus of pleasing their partner, they can act as a sex doll, having their partner's will inflicted upon them, knowing the bliss of surrender.

There is absolutely nothing wrong with being a Dominant or submissive. Desiring to be a Dominant does not mean you are bossy, controlling, or want to be in a mentally abusive relationship. On the same token, being submissive does not mean you are lazy or unwilling to contribute to your relationship. When done with consent and planning, a D/s sexual relationship is a joyous partnership to participate in. Both partners (assuming you're monogamous, and to save on word count, I'm going to refer to monogamous relationships from now on though these rules can easily apply to polyamorous relationships) will discover how much happier they are when their roles and boundaries are understood before sex even takes place. Sometimes during sex, there is a power struggle determining who will drive the action, take control, or dictate what happens next. In a D/s relationship, once the roles are understood and defined, that never happens.

One of the most important things to understand about D/s relationships is the roles never have to break down along gender lines. Archaic thinking would dictate the man is obviously the Dominant, and his female partner is automatically the submissive. Not even addressing the fact this discounts gay and lesbian couples, this narrow thinking can cause undue stress and anxiety for men who want to submit and for women who want to dominate. Let me make it perfectly clear, there is nothing wrong with a woman submitting or dominating, and the same applies to men as well as non-binary people.

You assume the role that makes you feel the most comfortable. Experiment with your partner. Tell each other how your role makes you feel. For those of you in a relationship with a female Dominant, you are experiencing femdom firsthand.

There is nothing intrinsically unique about submitting to a femdom. Women are just as capable as men when it comes to dominate their partners. What is unique about femdom is the cultural connotations around women. Many men find the idea of submitting to a woman absolutely tantalizing. Almost every culture portrays women as a passive, submissive gender, so the idea of a woman taking control of you may feel acutely erotic and taboo. It is a sad side effect of history, but many men find the prospect incredible. There are also men who are simply submissive, attracted to women, and prefer to have their female partner take control inside or outside the bedroom. This is what is known as a female-led relationship or FLR. Some men prefer FLR's for humiliation or because it suits their personality, neither of which is wrong as long as their female partner also enjoys their role in the relationship.

Chapter Two: Short History of Erotic Hypnosis

Before you can begin practicing hypnotic suggestion, it is important you understand where hypnosis came from and its storied history throughout the ages. Hypnosis has literally been around for thousands of years, but only received any kind of scientific scrutiny starting in the 1700s. The first known clinical use of hypnosis comes from what historians refer to as sleep temples that existed in ancient Egypt and ancient India over 4,000 years ago. These temples were a combination of church and hospital where a person was brought to pray and participate in a guided meditation in order to cure their afflictions in what is known as temple sleep.

The first medical journal to discuss hypnosis was written by the Persian physician Avicenna, known as The Book of Healing, which was published in 1027 C.E. Many people would be surprised to find out the use of hypnotism in western cultures completely revolved around magnets. This is where things get really interesting. A traveling Jesuit priest by the name of Father Maximillian Hell (who was not an anime villain but in fact, a traveling healer) used magnets to treat the ailments of his followers. This caught the attention of Franz Mesmer, who coined the term "animal magnetism" and who we derive the word 'mesmerized' from.

Franz Mesmer believed the same forces that dictated the tides also dictated our health, and those energies existed in our bodies. He believed by adjusting or balancing the amount of "animal magnetism" in our bodies, he could cure a variety of maladies. It is important to understand animal magnetism in his time did not mean what it means today. He was simply describing energy or fluid he couldn't observe or detect but still had a great influence on our wellbeing.

His therapy, which was called mesmerism™, involved the use of magnets to move and control the animal magnetism in a patient's body and improve their health. His unfounded theory later dictated he could simply use his bare hands in the place of magnets since he had so much animal magnetism he didn't require magnets to treat patients. This, as you can imagine, caused a lot of problems. In what is remarkably similar to a reiki session, Franz Mesmer would gently rub his hands over a patient. In some combination of hypnotic suggestion and the placebo effect, many of his patients claimed to have been treated successfully by Mesmer, though he was forced out of Vienna when he failed to heal a famous musician.

Things only became stranger from there. Franz moved to Paris, and as part of the aristocracy, thanks to his advantageous marriage, he would see as many as 400 rich and powerful clients in a single day. His mesmeric treatments were like something out of a Robert E. Howard short story. Patients would be tended to in his dimly lit salon flooded with burning incense. At the center of the room was a strange machine called a baquet filled with glass and scraps of iron. The baquet looked like a wooden bathtub flipped upside down with metal spider legs coming out of it. Patients would sit around the baquet and hold hands as Mesmer flitted around the room in a lavender wizard's robe and rubbed his magnetic wizard wand over his patients. Aren't you glad you read this book?

As you can imagine, this caused a few problems for our old friend Franz Mesmer. One of his clients at the time was a woman named Marie Antoinette. Yes, that Marie Antoinette, wife of King Louis XVI. Ole' Lou didn't really approve of this utter insanity and created multiple commissions charged with finding out if animal magnetism even existed, one of which included Benjamin Franklin. Franz was furious and refused to participate in their scientific trials. As you may have guessed, the scientific commissions could not find proof animal magnetism existed. Franz left the country and later died in obscurity.

Thankfully, a more scrupulous physician named James Braid saved hypnotism from dying in obscurity like alchemy or the zune. James Braid was a legitimate physician who did serious and credible research into the phenomenon we now know today as hypnosis and even coined the term "hypnosis." Braid first witnessed mesmerism™ during a traveling show, and the mesmerist there allowed him to observe the patients who were mesmerized. Disliking the charlatan connotations of mesmerism, Braid coined the term "neuro-hypnotism" before he realized hypnosis doesn't actually put you to sleep like previously believed. He wanted to call the phenomenon mono-ideism, but that doesn't have quite the same ring to it. Braid observed a changed in the mental countenance of patients who focused their eyesight on a single, bright point such as lamp, candle, or mirror, a technique still used by hypnotherapists today. Because of Braid's extensive research and willingness to discuss his findings, he singlehandedly rescued hypnosis from obscurity and is considered by many to be the father of hypnotism.

The earliest reference to erotic hypnosis I have been able to find comes from a 1963 book called Perverse Crimes in History, wherein Robert Masters suggests erotic hypnosis can be used to overcome sexual dysfunction resulting from trauma in addition to creating hands-free orgasms and vivid, erotic hallucinations. These claims should all be taken with a pinch of salt, but it would also be safe to say erotic hypnosis has lasted as long as clinical hypnosis itself, considering there were rumors Franz Mesmer used it for his own, personal sexual satisfaction on some of his female patients.

This is why knowing your history is so important. You must respect the process and understand how destructive it can be as well as the negative connotations surrounding hypnosis. If you purchased or borrowed this book, clearly, you have at least a passing interest in hypnosis, but should understand your partner might not feel the same way. That is why it is critical you come armed with pertinent information. Only relatively recently has hypnosis been seen as a legitimate treatment, and even less is known or understood about its erotic applications. With the writing of this book, I am hoping to shed more light on this greatly misunderstood phenomenon and create a positive sexual experience for you and your partner.

Chapter Three: How to Perform a Session

While no single book can give you all the information you need to be a professional hypnotherapist, that doesn't mean you can't pick up enough technique to reap noticeable benefit from personal erotic hypnosis sessions at home. Don't worry about your level of education or prior experience. For your purposes, a beginner's guide is enough to see results. As long as you aren't charging people for this service or purporting to treat illnesses, you'll be fine.

The most important thing you can do is read and re-read this chapter and practice constantly. Don't expect huge results in your first attempt. Erotic hypnosis is a delicate yet intensive procedure. You could do everything right, but your partner may be unable to focus or have other worries on their minds. If you are unsuccessful your first time, that doesn't mean you will never be successful. There are other sources of learning besides this book.

I think one of the most important things we pick up as functioning adults, and a sign of confidence and trustworthiness is to go out and do our own research. No one book has all the answers. You found an excellent, approachable book to start with, but there are more intensive guides to further your learning. I'm so confident in the information presented in this book. I want you to go out and compare what I have told you what others have said in the field of erotic hypnosis. Don't take anything I say at face value. With those caveats out of the way, let's breakdown the steps of a successful hypnosis session.

Negotiate Limits and Boundaries

Before every single erotic hypnosis session, no matter how familiar you are with your partner, always check in to confirm where you and your partner's boundaries are. This is applicable even when you aren't practicing hypnosis. No matter how vanilla you consider your sex life, it is paramount you check in frequently to make sure both of you are comfortable with plans and past experiences.

Imagine if your partner felt stress and anxiety at the thought of being hypnotized, but you never gave them the opportunity to speak up until afterward? That would be a miserable experience for them and could sour them to ever participating again. Especially when it comes to surrendering power or control (in this case in the form of hypnotic suggestion), it is critical you and your partner are on the same page. Never attempt to force a nervous or unwilling participant into erotic hypnosis. If they are uncomfortable, then it is inappropriate to try.

In addition to establishing ease and comfort, limits, and safe words should be implemented as well. Discuss with your partner beforehand what they will be willing and unwilling to do under the influence of hypnotic suggestion. Typically you will receive a shortlist of undesirable tasks, but your partner is allowed as many limits as they need. In my experience, I find it helpful to establish soft limits and hard limits. Soft limits are generally kinkier things that require a certain mood (such as a hypnotic trance) in order to enjoy and participate in. These limits can be broken with your partner's permission. Hard limits, on the other hand, cannot be broken under any circumstances, and it is considered a massive violation of trust to do so.

Also, keep in mind the hypnotist has the same limits and right of refusal as their partner. If a hypnotist is uncomfortable making their partner perform a certain action or giving a specific suggestion, they are absolutely allowed to refuse. Limits are about comfort. They are not resources to be negotiated in your favor. Respect your partner and their desires.

Even when limits are established, events can transpire, which require an immediate pause in erotic activity. If someone develops anxiety or pain during a session, they need a way to stop it immediately. Saying 'no' or 'stop' is not sufficient as many people enjoy saying those things in the throes of passion for heightening forbidden feelings. To be safe, you and your partner should establish a safe word. Ideally, one or two syllables, something easy to pronounce, and a word that would not occur naturally during sex. In addition to a safe word, those practicing hypnosis should also have what is called a safe gesture. People who have been under the influence of hypnosis sometimes describe an inability to form words or conjure the word they wish to speak. In this circumstance, a distinct gesture should be employed if they find their situation untenable. Snapping fingers, clapping, or pulling your ear lobe are all simple gestures that can be employed as safe gestures to pause the action.

Induce a Trance

Each piece of the hypnosis procedure is equally important. When people think of hypnosis, they think of putting people into a trance, but negotiating comfort, implanting suggesting, and providing aftercare are crucial components of the erotic hypnosis process. Don't focus all your attention on induction and neglect the other pieces of the process.

The key component of induction is relaxation. Your goal during this phase of erotic hypnosis is to make your partner more relaxed and comfortable than they have ever been before and to eliminate any possible worries or distractions. To start, focus on physical relaxation, which can help with mental relaxation when it comes later. Have them lay or sit in their most comfortable position possible. This can be sitting on the couch, reclining in an armchair, or lying in bed. The exact position is not important, and everyone is different. What is important is they are as comfortable as possible. The last thing you want is for your partner to be thinking about back, foot, or shoulder pain when you are trying to induce a trance.

Some hypnotists use incense or candles as part of the relaxation process, but bear in mind you'll be using a scent as a focal point if you choose to do so. Either way, start by having your partner take a deep breath in through their nose and out through their mouth. Have them repeat this process several times. Let them take several deep breaths and gently bring them to a normal level of breathing. As you talk them through this, steadily lower the volume of your voice. Slow your cadence. This is a subconscious cue for them to relax. As you talk slower and gentler, subconsciously, they will become even more relaxed and move to a trance state. What you are essentially doing is making them more relaxed than they have ever been before.

To help relax their mind, have them focus on their breathing. Repeat this simple mantra, becoming quieter, and soft-spoken as the chant goes on, "Breath in through your nose, out through your mouth. In through your nose, out through your mouth." Repeat this several times. Then have them focus on their breathing. Direct them to focus their attention on the sound of their breathing, how the healing air relaxes their muscles and lowers their heart rate. Then put intense focus on the sound of breathing and only the sound.

One of the common pitfalls of hypnosis is when a practitioner instructs their subject to clear their mind. It's important to hypnotic implant suggestions, but human beings are absolutely terrible at clearing their minds. Your brain wants to think every second of every day. You must give your partner something incredibly simple and present to think about. Their focus can literally be anything as long as it's simple and doesn't raise questions when they think about it. You can have them focus on a candle, a piece of jewelry, a handkerchief, but not something like a song or painting, which might amplify their imagination instead of taming it.

At this point, your partner should be partially or fully induced in a hypnotic trance. To go all the way, you must enact a process called deepening. Now that they are relaxed and focused have them become even more relaxed and focused.

A strong technique for ultimate relaxation is what is called a body scan. Start at their toes, and describe to them an intense sensation of comfort and relaxation. Move to the feet, the ankles, shins, knees, thighs, hips, groin, stomach, chest, arms, you get the picture. Go slow. Take as much time as possible. Hypnosis is not about a quick fix. The slower and quieter you go, the more effective your deepening will be. At this point, your partner should be in a state of ultimate relaxation.

To focus their attention even more intensely, have them focus on what is called sub modalities. Sub modalities are a subset of the five primary senses. If focusing on a candle, focus on how bright it is, how it flickers, how small or large it is, specifically the flame. You are evaporating all their errant thoughts, which make hypnosis difficult and instead of having them focus on one thing with the utmost intensity. You are opening their mind up to receiving suggestions.

Hypnotic Suggestion

After relaxing their body and focusing their mind, now you can begin the process of hypnotic suggestion. This is the portion of hypnosis where your creativity can run wild. Bearing in mind, this book is designed for femdom erotic hypnosis, there are several strategies for making the most of your suggestions.

One technique is amplifying arousal. Create a series of associations with your partner to immerse them in female domination and your female further led relationship. Below are three suggestions you can use for positive association, but feel free to create your own.

- *"When you think of being dominated by women, you will feel intense erotic excitement."*
- *"Being in a female-led relationship fills you with joy and contentment."*
- *"The idea of being controlled by a woman causes you great arousal."*

Your goal is to create positive associations with female domination and heighten the erotic response your partner has to it. If your partner responds to aspects of BDSM like impact play, bondage, or humiliation, you can also create positive associations with these practices as well.

Another technique of hypnotic suggestion is guided visualization. Instead of implanting suggestions, you are implanting fantasies into your partner. This leaves room for limitless creativity and imagination, and the next chapter is completely dedicated to effectively creating your own script to recite to your partner.

Another technique you may enjoy is the implementation of triggers. Triggers are objects or actions that will trigger an erotic response in your partner. They can be new triggers, or you can reinforce triggers your partner already enjoys. Here are some examples.

- *"When you see me wear my red lipstick, you will feel submissive towards me."*
- *"When I put on my black corset, you will obey my every command."*

- *"You will become aroused whenever you think about submitting to me."*

The final technique involves creating new kinks in your partner. Just because your partner doesn't currently find a certain thing, erotic doesn't mean they can't be made to. Erotic hypnosis is the perfect technique for opening up their sexual palette. Try a few of these suggestions next time your partner is in a trance.

- *"From now on, you will find powerful women intensely erotic."*
- *"You will now find sexual arousal whenever you please me."*
- *"The idea of submitting to me fills you with sexual energy."*

An important thing to keep in mind when inducing a trance or to give hypnotic suggestions is that hypnosis will not work every time it is performed, especially when you and your partner are new to it. Some people simply cannot be hypnotized because they are too willful or doubtful of the process. Others may experience too much stress and anxiety on a certain night. Your partner may be worrying about other things or experience physical pain during a session. It may take several attempts to experience noticeable results. What is important is that you practice and learn all you can learn about hypnosis.

Aftercare

After any kind of sexual activity, it is of critical importance to provide aftercare for your partner. To bring them out of their trance, guide them back to a state of normalcy, returning their mental and physical sensations back to where you started before the session. It can be helpful to count them down as they leave their trance and finish with a clap or snap of your fingers, signaling to their brain the session is over.

If hypnosis becomes too effective, you may have to wipe suggestions from their minds. If your partner becomes too aroused but certain objects or actions, you might have to dismiss those suggestions before your hypnosis session ends. For example, "My knee-high boots no longer make you feel submissive."

Once your partner is out of their trance, they may not experience anything at all, or they may experience intense emotions. It is of critical importance you provide them physical and emotional comfort as they come out of their hypnosis session. This is what is known in the BDSM community as aftercare. Power exchanges can serve well up all kinds of intense emotions in a person, and it is your sworn duty as their sexual partner to provide them comfort if they need it. Make sure you schedule enough time in your session for aftercare. This is not a process that can be simply glossed over.

Even if your partner did not need aftercare during a previous session, they might require it this time or after a future session. The offer should always be on the table. There is no shame in needing to be comforted and reassured. Aftercare is an excellent time to bond with your partner outside a sexual setting. Have blankets and videos ready. Sometimes you may need to take their mind off their current emotions, so their favorite TV show or streaming series may afford an excellent distraction. Some subs become hungry or exhausted after a particularly long session. There's no reason not to stock up on their favorite foods and feed them afterward.

Hypnotic sessions can feel like an intense journey for the participants, both physically and emotionally. It is important you have comforts such as bedding, food, TV, and even stuffed animals close at hand should your submissive need them. This is not some afterthought you can choose not to participate in. Not only do you have a responsibility to comfort your partner after distress you advertently or inadvertently caused, but aftercare is also an integral part of the sexual experience. If you fail to provide these comforts after such an arduous emotional journey, you run the risk of damaging your relationship. You may also lose the chance of ever performing hypnosis again if you fail to be reliable when your partner comes out of their trance. All four portions of the hypnosis process are equally important. While induction and suggestion require specific technique and practice to master, negotiation and aftercare are simple tasks you should easily be able to provide.

Chapter Four: How to Write Your Own Hypnosis Script

Writing your own hypnosis script is not as difficult as you may initially believe. Even if you've never written anything since high school, anyone can write an effective hypnosis script with a few rules and techniques. You absolutely don't have to worry about grammar, spelling, or punctuation as you and your partner will be the only ones who ever see it.

Before I lay some tips on you, I'd like to suggest that if you're the hypnotist in your partnership, don't have your partner write the script. If your subject writes the script, their brain will be anticipating what is going to be said next instead of focusing on the words currently being said. Much in the same way that highly effective relaxation tracks contain no lyrics and don't repeat sections of melody, your subject should be focused on the meaning and effect of the words instead of the words themselves. They can offer suggestions about what they would like to see in a script, but having them write or co-write the script can reduce the effectiveness.

A large portion of the script involves retreading the techniques from the previous chapter. Feel free to mix and match induction techniques from earlier. Body scans and countdowns are effective and proven ways to induce a trance. Don't feel like you're cheating or being lazy by using the same induction techniques over and over. If a technique has proven effectiveness in your relationship, stick with it. There's no reason to change things out of some misguided obligation to avoid lazy writing. While I cannot give advice or advocate selling hypnosis scripts, for the purposes of your sexual relationship, repeating induction techniques is suitable for recreational purposes.

Bear in mind some induction techniques might be more effective when combined with certain suggestions and less effective when combined with others. Practice and experimentation are key to the effective technique as well as effective scripts. Don't put any pressure on yourself to get this perfect immediately. If you've never written a hypnosis script before, how can you expect to be great at it your first time?

Once you are satisfied with your induction, now you must consider what suggestions you would like to get across. As stated in the previous chapter, you have multiple styles of suggestion you can focus on or mix and match. Simple suggestions may involve reinforcing ideas and kinks your partner already finds arousing. Other suggestions may involve creating new associations between objects and behavior with sexual arousal. Finally, you can create a guided experience for your partner. One of the most intense things about hypnosis is how powerful visualizations become during a trance. This isn't simply sight and sound but all kinds of sensations, both physical and emotional.

Writing a script beforehand is an excellent way to create a vivid fantasy for your partner instead of relying on spontaneous creativity at the moment. With a script, you won't stumble or slow down as you struggle to continue their fantasy in their minds. Plus, with a script, you can practice in private or even memorize your words as if they were lines in a play. Some people prefer to spontaneously guide a fantasy, while others swear by a script. Neither is incorrect, and different things work for different people.

When creating a guided fantasy, this is an excellent time to get input from your sub. Find out what their fantasies are and have them describe their fantasies with as much detail as possible. When hypnosis is at its most effective, it can feel like you're really there inside the fantasy and experience the same emotions and physical sensations as if you really had a sexual encounter.

The Language of a Script

If there was a surefire way to be an excellent writer, there wouldn't be so many crappy books in circulation. You have the benefit of only needing to please one reader, in this case, a listener. As stated before, practice and experimentation lead to better scripts. But as you write, you should focus on the language of your script. Some professionals disdain the use of overly floral or descriptive language, but in a hypnotic script, that is exactly what you need to aim for. As a general rule of thumb, you want to focus on the five senses to make the experience as vivid as possible. The more senses you engage, the more your sub will feel like they are really there.

In addition to the five senses, also engage the sub modalities. Don't just focus on what they're seeing, but how big something is, how dark a room is, how soft something is, and the sensation of time passing.

The utmost importance should be placed on the sexual and emotional feelings of an experience. These hypnotic suggestions are designed to elicit a sexual and emotional response in your sub, but remember, they are in a trance and open to broader suggestions. With effective hypnosis, you can implant feelings of arousal in your sub without describing anything erotic. If they desire to feel small, weak, or feminine, describe those feelings to them. Effective hypnosis is about combining the feelings with the thoughts that generate those feelings. You're pushing on them from separate sides in order to create an intense swirl of emotional and sexual experience like a crucible in their mind.

Finally, be sure to leave room in your script for aftercare. You need to bring them out of their trance with all the care you used to put them in. Focus on soothing and pleasant emotions. Make their feelings and suggestions mild to help them cope with what they're experiencing. Take your time. There is no rush when it comes to hypnosis.

In our final three chapters, you will be able to read and use scripts already prepared for you and your partner. Feel free to alter these scripts to suit your needs, but remember the importance of good technique. Suggestions are not effective before inducing a trance, and aftercare is critical for the wellbeing of your partner.

Chapter Five: Femdom Script one

"Breath in through your nose and out through your mouth. Breathe in through your nose and out through your mouth. In through your nose, out through your mouth. In through your nose, out through your mouth. Breathe in...And out. Breathe in...And out. Breathe slowly. A gentle breath.

"You slowly feel yourself becoming relaxed. Your body is gently relaxed. Just a little bit. Your tense muscles are loosening. The tension in your legs and back are easing. Feel the healing blood flow move through your muscles, easing pain and tension. Feel relaxation wash over you like a warm tide. The warmth starts in your toes. Imagine each of your toes alive with gentle warmth, relaxing. The warmth spreads through your feet, releasing ache and tension. Relaxation moves through your legs, easing your muscles. Your knees heal and relax. Feel the tension ease in your hips and back. Warmth spreads and relaxes you. Feel the rush of warm energy to your cock/pussy. Feel your sexual energy spark and smolder as your body receives healing warmth. The warm, healing energy moves up your back. Your back relaxes, your shoulders rest, and you are completely relaxed. The muscles in your neck relax. You are soft, warm, and feel amazing. Amazing warmth floods through your body. Your face and ears filled with warmth. Your entire body is filled with warmth, washing over you.

"Imagine lying down in the surf, and warm ocean waves wash over you. Warm water gently cascading over your naked body, easing your pain and tension. Warm ocean waves enveloping you. The waves come and wash the pain out. The waves come in and out. In...and out. In...and out.

"You can feel your body floating. Floating on warm water, you are completely at rest. Your body is more relaxed than it has ever been before. Every muscle and joint in your body is loose. Loose like warm water running over smooth rocks. You are at peace. You are comfortable. You know comfort. You gently float down a warm stream knowing complete peace and comfort.

"Imagine the stream. Clearwater whispers over smooth stone. Focus on the water. Focus only on the water. The water is clear. Focus on the murmur as it flows over smooth stones. The gentle warm water flows. Focus on the clear water flowing. It flows. Focus your mind. Focus on the flowing, clear water. Focus. Take a deep breath in through your nose and out through your mouth. Breathe for me. Focus on the clear water flowing. Your mind is a clear stream flowing freely. Focus on the clear water. Take a deep breath. In through your nose, out through your mouth. Focus on the clear stream.

"Focus your mind. Focus on the stream. Your mind is a clear running stream. Relax. Open yourself up. Open yourself to my suggestions. You are more relaxed than you have ever been before, and your mind is open to me. Your mind is open to me. Focus on the sound of my voice. Focus on my voice. Focus...on my voice. Listen to the sound of my voice. Listen. You will obey the sound of my voice. You will obey my words. My words will become your thoughts. Listen to my words. Listen. Listen. Listen.

"You are feeling submissive. In your heart and mind, you can feel submission blooming like a beautiful flower. Your deepest desire is to submit to me. You were born to submit, and you have chosen to submit to me. You are submissive, and that makes you beautiful. In your heart, you know you are a submissive. Feel the weight of my authority over you like a heavy blanket. The blanket is warm and comforts you. It weighs you down. Feel how heavy it is. You are warm and comforted under the weight of my authority. In your heart, you feel peace and comfort when you submit to me.

"You feel weaker. You feel the weight of my dominance, pushing you under me. You give yourself freely to me. Feel your weakness, your lack of strength. Feel yourself weakening. Relish in how delicate you feel. You are a beautiful submissive, weak, vulnerable, and free. Feel the weakness and submission move through your body. You will submit to me and only me. Your muscles are soft, and your body yields to me.

"When you hear the sound of my voice, you will feel submissive. When you see me, you will feel submissive. When you think about me, you will feel submissive. When you think about women, you will feel submissive. Breathe in through your nose, out through your mouth, and know these words as truths. I control your thoughts, and I control your breathing. You belong to me. You are my submissive, and you belong to me. You live to submit. You were born to submit. Submit to me.

"Your mind and body are compelled to obey me. In your heart, you obey me. My voice carries the authority of instruction, and you feel compelled to obey. The sight and sound of women make you feel compelled to obey. Focus on my voice. Do not challenge the things I say. Give yourself completely unto me. Obey.

"When you kneel for me, you will experience intense feelings of submission. You will feel like a slave, and I will feel like your master. You were born to kneel. Kneeling for me, feels like a second skin. Nothing in the world feels more right than kneeling for me. When you kneel, your body will be flooded with an intense need to submit to me. Embrace that feeling. Submit.

"Let that weakness fill you up. Feel the sensation of submission flood your veins. Every part of your body desires to submit to my will. Let your mind flood with thoughts of submission. Every thought should be about pleasing me. Devote your body and mind to my pleasure. Obey me.

"Whenever you think erotic thoughts, you will only think of me. Whenever you wish to masturbate, you will masturbate to me. I am in control of your thoughts and actions now. When you think of submission, you will think of me.

"Now come back to me. You are a whole and bound submissive. Rise up from your trance. Your body is returning to normal. Feel the normal sensation of being a return to your nerves. Feel your mind readjust to being normal once again. From now, you will function once again like a normal person, but when your thoughts turn to kink and eroticism, you will be enraptured at the thought of submitting to me. Feel your body awaken. Let your normal thoughts flow once more. You are coming back to me. Feel your mind and body come alive again.

"When I snap my fingers, you will return to normal."

Chapter Six:
Feminization Script

"You are feeling restful. Let your eyes grow heavy. Your eyes are so heavy you cannot lift them. Relax your body. Take a deep breath. In through your nose...and out through your mouth. In through your nose and out through your mouth. Breath deep. Feel your body growing heavier. You are on the edge of sleep. Fully rested but awake. Take a deep breath in, and exhale. In...and out. In...and out. Focus on your breathing. Listen to the air, enter your body...and listen to it leave. Focus only on the sound of your own breathing. Breathe in...and out. In through your nose...and out through your mouth. In...and out. In...and out.

"Your entire body is relaxed. Feel every muscle in your body go slack as you enter into a state of ultimate relaxation. Relax...and breathe. In...and out. In...and out. Focus on the sound of your breathing as every muscle in your body relaxes. In...and out. In...and out.

"I'm going to count down now. At the end of the countdown, your body will be in a state of perfect relaxation. Ten, your body is heavy, and your muscles are relaxed. Remember to breath. In...and out. Nine, relaxation washes over you like an awesome wave. Any aches or pains you are experiencing begin to recede. Breathe in and out. Eight, your muscles are filled with healing warmth. You are melting into the chair/bed/couch. Seven, take another deep breath and feel the tension escape from your lungs. Feel the healing air enter your body. Six, you are gently falling deeper into comfort. Imagine your body enveloped by soft, warm pillows. Imagine ultimate comfort. Five, your comfort. Your body is synonymous with comfort and relaxation. Four, you can no longer feel your body. Focus on the sound of my voice. Three, you are weightless, floating in the air. There is no pressure or discomfort. Two, you are coming down, deep down. One, you are ready to receive.

"Imagine a dress. Imagine a dress that would look beautiful on you. The dress is short and shows off your legs. Your legs are hairless. Imagine the dress. The dress is bright pink with white trim. The dress is beautiful. Imagine tiny pink bows on the waist and hem of the skirt. Imagine yourself wearing the dress. Focus all your attention on the dress. Imagine your hairless chest exposed in the low cut dress. Focus on the dress. Imagine the soft, pink material pressed against your skin. It is a beautiful dress. Focus on the saturated pink, the softness of the fabric. Imagine how beautiful you would be in the dress. Focus on the dress. It is so pink. It draws everyone's attention. You are beautiful and feminine. Focus on the dress. The dress is your identity. It gives you freedom. Imagine how beautiful the dress is.

"Now imagine how you feel in the dress. Imagine femininity like a glorious flower blossoming inside your chest. Imagine how good it feels to be feminine. This glory inside yourself, awakening like the rising sun. The feeling is so warm and beautiful; it overwhelms you. You are lost in the femininity. Your body and hair conform to your feminine thoughts. Your hair is long and shiny, beautiful, lush, rich. Your skin is soft, smooth, and hairless. Everyone thinks you are beautiful and feminine. Imagine the beautiful, perfect you.

"Submitting makes you feel feminine. Submitting makes you feel more feminine than anything else in the world. When you submit to me, your inner girl screams out in ecstasy in relief. The girl inside you finally has someone to give herself to. Every iota of your being wants to submit to me because I make you feel more feminine than anything else in the world. Submit to me.

"When you obey my commands, you feel supremely feminine. When you bend over for me, that makes you feel feminine. When you undress for me, femininity explodes through your body. When my hand touches your skin, your heart fills with girlish nature. Give yourself to me. Obey me. Submit to me.

"Wearing panties makes you feel beautiful and important. Having your cock pressed against the inside of your panties makes you feel like a little princess. Let that feeling wash over you and envelope you. When I reach my hand in your panties, you feel small, weak, and helpless. Let those small feelings lower you and submit yourself to me. Being feminine makes you feel amazing. You feel more beautiful than you have ever felt in your entire life. You feel delicate like the petals of a flower. So easy to crush, but you stand up straight. Nothing has ever felt more right in your entire life. You feel weak like a little puppy, but you do not feel wrong. Your weakness is an act of freedom. No one requires strength and determination from you. You are free to be yourself. When you are with me, you feel safe. When you are in my embrace, you feel safe. Your weakness allows others to give you comfort. You feel helpless. You are not lost, but for the first time in your life, you are truly found. Because of me, you have the freedom to feel helpless.

"You now know true freedom. You now know true femininity. Everything you have experienced in your life before this moment now makes sense. Look at yourself and know that you are beautiful and loved for who you are. No shame, no guilt, only freedom. You are a beautiful flower and deserve to be cherished.

"Now, I need you to come back to me. Hold onto all the feelings that make you feel beautiful and special. Those feelings matter. But I need you to come back to me. You're going to leave this trance feeling beautiful and rested. I will count you down. Ten, you are feeling more awake. Energy gently buzzes through your body. Nine, you are rested but are coming back to wakefulness. Feel sensation return to your body. Eight, energy is welling up from your toes and rising through your body. Seven, your mind is coming back to me. Your thought patterns are returning to normal. Six, you are you again, the sensation is returning to your legs and hips. Feel the natural flow of blood through your veins. Five, you are close to wakefulness. Energy and alertness are returning. Four, you are so close to full wakefulness. Your mind is sharpening, and your five senses are returning. Three, come back to me; you are awake, feel, and see the room around you. Two, you are with me now, safe here. I am here to comfort you. One, when I clap my hands, you will completely come back to me.

Chapter Seven: The Sensual Script

Hey. How are you? I really mean that. How are you? Maybe a little tense, and not in a good way. Don't worry. I'm going to fix that. I understand how you feel, right now. Maybe it's been a really long day, and you've worked really hard. Or maybe your day's only getting started. Maybe your day has been boring, and uneventful, and you're looking to feel a bit better. No worries. One way or another, you're here, right now, because you've finally got some alone time. You can finally be by yourself, and just relax, as you give in to the sound of my voice, washing over your body, from the top of your head to the tips of your toes, wave after wave, relaxing you, helping you sink deeper, and further into blissful relaxation.

Give in to the feeling. Right now, it's just you and me. There's nothing else, and no one else. Just us. Alone. How does that make you feel? What if I told you that I could make you feel even better than you already do? Would you like to make me happy? I love it when my boy toys do everything I say. That makes me happy. Very, very happy. So close your eyes. There. Good boy. I want you to pay attention to the sound of my voice. Just focus on everything I'm saying, and nothing else. Nothing matters right now, than the sound of me, in your ears, gently guiding you to open yourself up to my words. There. Perfect.

There's nowhere for you to be than this moment, right here, right now. Feel how perfect the moment is, with just us two together. Now, I want you to breath in, deep, and slow. Nice. Hold it. Keep holding it. Part your lips ever so slightly. Now, go on and exhale through those luscious lips of yours. Beautiful. Focus on here and now. Focus on the sound of my voice, as I lead you deeper, deeper, deeper still, into complete relaxation. Focus on my voice, as I lead you to a state of blissful surrender. Now, you're going to take another long, deep breath for me. Make it nice and deep. As deep as you can. And then hold it for just three counts, before you exhale, nice and slow, through those parted lips of yours. Are you ready? Good boy.

Breathe in, now. There. That's it. Let your lungs fill completely. Let your stomach rise ever so gently. Now, hold it. Hold it. Hold it. And release, through your lips, feeling your body as all the knots and tense spots unwind. Notice how relaxed and at ease you feel, and how your mind follows my voice more eagerly. Keep breathing like this. Inhale deep through your nose, hold it for three counts, and then exhale nice and long through your lips, until your lungs empty out. I love it when you breathe this way. It makes you feel so good, doesn't it? You feel even better as you listen to my voice. Keep breathing slowly, deeply, as you unwind. Bask in the sound of my voice, enveloping you like a comfortable cocoon. Just relax, listen, and follow the suggestions I give you.

With each breath, your body and mind will be more relaxed than ever. As soon as you're ready to let go completely, feel yourself fade into my voice. That's it. Meld with me. Now, as you keep breathing nice, and slow, I want you to imagine yourself just the way you are, in this moment. See yourself in your mind's eye. Notice how relaxed you are. Notice how your eyes are shut, and you look so still, so calm. Now, in your mind, see a ball of white light floating right over your belly. It's warm, and makes you sink impossibly deeper into relaxation. Feel this ball of white light as it washes over your whole body with a pleasant warmth. Feel the gentle heat as it moves outward, from your belly, to the crown of your head and the soles of your feet.

Now, notice your feet. Feel the warm light gently washing away all the stress and tension in your feet. Let yourself give in to the delicious heat, as it seeps into your bones and muscles. As you breathe in, notice the ball of white light enveloping your feet completely in utter and complete relaxation. Notice this happening, in your mind's eye, and feel your body as your feet are drained of every form of tension. As you breathe in, allow the warm, delicious relaxation you feel to go deeper and deeper, seeping into the muscles of your feet. As you breathe out, notice even more tension leaving your body. That's it. Very good.

Now, notice the warm light as it gently moves up to your shins. Notice as it gets to your knees. See that glorious, white ball of light and warmth, as it gently massages your legs, massaging them so that the tension just melts away. Feel that gentle, deliciously decadent heat as it moves from your knees, right to your thighs. As you breathe out, allow the tension to go. Feel the warmth from the ball of white light, as it completely relaxes your legs. You're doing well. Really well.

Allow the ease and relaxation you feel in your lower body to move back up to your belly. See the ball of white light in your mind's eye, hovering over your belly. Feel its warmth, as it gently caresses your stomach, causing you to feel sweet relaxation in your stomach. Let that heat permeate your very center, taking over you, making you feel even more relaxed, even more at ease than you ever imagined possible. Allow the muscles in your core to unwind, relax, let loose. Feel the tension in your belly disappear into nothingness.

Breath in. Nice. Deep. Slow. Allow the light to move ever so gently onto your spine. Allow that feeling of warmth and relaxation to move to your lower back. Let the feeling of ease move from there into your shoulders. Let it gently caress your neck. That's it. You can feel the heat, as it spreads all over you, up and down. You can feel all the tension in your spine melting away. You can feel your shoulders, more relaxed than they have ever been. As you listen to the sound of my voice, you allow yourself to go deeper, deeper, deeper still into complete relaxation.

Now, feel the warmth from this glorious, white ball of light, as it moves into your chest, making the muscles in your chest completely relax. You feel the heat as it moves around your lungs, and your heart, filling you with so much peace and calm. Now, breathe, nice and slow, allowing my voice to relax you even more. Allow the ball of light to relax you even further, as you feel the warmth move from your shoulders, down both your arms. Feel your upper arms as all the tension melts away. Feel the warmth from the ball as it relaxes your wrists, and your fingertips. As you feel your hands become more and more relaxed, you might notice there's a slight tingle in them. Breathe. Keep breathing. As you breathe in, allow the warmth from the ball of white light to completely wash over your face, and your head. Feel the muscles in your cheeks and your scalp, as they become loose, and relaxed. Feel your jaw muscles, as they unclench, and hang loose. Feel the bliss that envelopes your whole body, now. Allow yourself to let go, and surrender to sweet, delicious sleep. Go on. Feel how safe and supported you are, as you listen to the sound of my voice. Allow yourself to be taken by blissful sleep. Breathe in, nice and deep. Feel that comforting warmth working its way into you, deeper, deeper still, making you feel completely relaxed. Feel the heat as it gently settles on your groin. Notice the way the warmth spreads right into your cock, down the shaft, and through your balls. Feel how relaxing that is. Feel the warmth completely taking over you, making you feel rested, ecstatic, at ease. Give in to the pleasure you feel within you, now. Allow each breath relax you, and arouse you. Yes. You feel it, don't you? Feel the relaxation and pleasure as it spreads from the very crown of your head, to the tops of your toes. Give in to the pleasure you feel. Let it own you. Surrender to it. Surrender to my voice. Surrender to me. Good. You're mine now. I am not one to share. So hear yourself respond with a "yes," in your mind, when I say, you are mine. You are mine. Good.

You know, a lot of people have the wrong idea about being submissive. They think it's wrong for a man to be dominated. They think only animals, idiots, and people who are worthless are the only ones who would allow themselves to be submissive. But that's not true. You're not like that. In fact, you could be very intelligent. You could have an amazing sense of humor. You could be a master in your field, conquering your world, day after day. You might even be a very dominant force to reckon with in other aspects of your life. Breathe in, nice and deep. Now, breathe out. Very good.

Now, I want to be very clear, my pet: It doesn't matter what kind of role you play in public. It doesn't matter how you're thought of in your social circles. You see, you, my pet, are a very complex man. There's more to you than meets the eye. The fact of the matter is that even the most dominant of men has a side to him that is submissive, willing to be bent to the will of his domina. I want you to know that this is completely natural. As natural as the delicious heat you feel between your legs. Breathe in. Feel the pleasure between your legs, for a moment. Now, breathe out, and relax.

It's natural to be submissive. This submissive, obedient side of you, is what allows you to play in a world of fantasy. A world where you can escape from the shackles of reality. A world where you don't need to deal with anger, and you never have to be stressed. A world where you do not have any obligations to stick with, or any decisions to make. In this world that I am creating for you, my pet, you do not have to deal with the burden of being in charge. You get the exquisite pleasure of being able to let go. You can become drunk on the wine of freedom which I offer you. So drink from me, as much as you want. Go on. Breathe in. Hold it. Now, breathe out. Very good. You do well with instructions. I like that. Very much. Look at how relaxed you are. You've been so focused on my voice, letting it soothe you, tease you, caress you. I like that.

Come back to your breath, now. Focus on it. Focus on the way your body feels, too. If you want to feel free, you must be willing to let go. Would you like to be free? Of course, you would. So go on and take a deep breath. Fill your lungs, generously. When you breathe out, let your breath go, along with your thoughts, and your need to control. Let go of your need to be in control, with each exhale, and with each inhale, let me into you, deeper, deeper, and deeper still. We're going to repeat this. Breathe in as deep as you can. Now hold it. Now, exhale, nice and slow, through your slightly parted lips, and notice how even more tension leaves your body. You have no worries. You have no expectations. You have no obligations. Just lie here with me for this moment, and enjoy the way you feel. Enjoy the way we feel together. Enjoy yourself, as you feel your dominant self become nonexistent. Enjoy the feeling of being replaced by your more obedient, more submissive side, as you let go. Drink from my cup of freedom. Drink from me, and allow your mind and body to be free. Allow yourself to be free, to be mine.

Breathe nice and deep. When you're ready, when you're willing, let go completely of your dominant side as you exhale, and then as you inhale, fully embrace and embody your submissive side. It's a wonderful part of you. It deserves to get some attention, too. Embrace it. Your submissive side is the reason you're able to experience the craziest, and the wildest of your dreams. Your submissive side allows you to be truly, deeply happy. It's the side that lets any and all of your fantasies come alive, so easily, since you are finally free of the shackles of being dominant. You are free to explore your most delicious, decadent, deepest, darkest fantasies with me. We're going to have a lot of fun, you and me.

Breathe in, through your nose. Hold it. Hold it just a bit, and now breathe out through your slightly parted lips. Relax into how good you feel right now. Let me take you on a delicious journey, with my words, with my voice, as it caresses your ears, going straight into your subconscious mind, which will do all the work for you as it processes my orders, while you just relax.

Now, I want you to lick your lips. There's a good boy. See how easy that was? You obeyed me, without even a second thought. Breathe in, as my words relax you, deeply, thoroughly. Now, there's something I want you to do for me. It's nothing complicated. I promise. As we spend time together like this, I'm going to ask you some questions, here and there. They're easy to answer, so relax, and breathe. The only answer you're allowed to give to these questions is yes. Just yes. Nothing more, nothing less. When I ask you, you must answer me clearly in your mind. You must answer me with pure conviction. When I say "well slave," you must respond out loud with the words "Yes, mistress." I want a loud yes, my pet. Is that clear? Well slave... You're catching on. I like that.

Just listen to my words, and allow them to show you that place of utter tranquility and deep, soothing relaxation, where you feel nothing but pure, unbridled passion and joy. Remember, whatever I ask you, you will answer me in your head with a clear yes, and whenever I say "well slave" you must respond out loud, "Yes, mistress." Now let's get some practice in.

My pet, are you right on the very edge of falling into a deep, deep trance? Well slave. That's very good. Once you're completely sunken in the trance, and you come into my world of complete domination, will you be a good pet and obey every single command that these lips of mine give you? Well slave. That's very good. Now that you've become the perfect, pliable, obedient little slave that you know you truly are, keep in mind that each time you are submissive, you submit to me, and none other. You want nothing more than to worship me, as your goddess. You want so badly to serve me in whatever way I deem fit, every day, no questions asked.

You want to offer up your body and mind to me in sacrifice, for me to do whatever I want, and play with in whatever way I deem fit. You can feel yourself getting aroused at the thought of being sexually submissive to me, don't you? Well slave. Of course you do. You can think of nothing else than all the fantasies you have in your head about submitting to me. You can barely contain the pleasure and excitement you feel, knowing your domina is very happy with you, and possibly incredibly turned on by the thought of you giving her your body and mind, your sexual energy, for her to use however she pleases. Am I correct, my pet? Well slave. I will use you to my heart's content. Rest assured. Listen to my words, as they permeate your mind, as you respond to them, instantly, easily, and gladly.

Now, I've got something a little special planned for you, but first things first, I want you to notice your delicious, naked body, as it lies on your bed, right now. Notice how relaxed and incredibly at ease it feels. Now, for only a few seconds, I want you to tighten the muscles in your body. Come along with me, my pet. Start from your toes. Curl them. Hold them that way. Flex your calves. Flex those thighs for me. Keep the tension as we move on to your glorious chest. Flex and tighten your pecs. Lovely. Ball both your hands into fists, and make your arms tense. Hold all these muscles, keep them nice and tense. Feel them tremble under the strain. And now, let go. Allow all of that tension to just melt away into nothing. Feel your muscles get completely limp. Well slave. That was good. We're going to do this one more time, my pet.

Begin again with your feet. Curl your toes, and make them nice and tense. Hold the tension as you move on to your calves, and make them tense. Hold the tension as you move on to your legs. Flex the muscles of your legs for me. Your thighs. Make them nice and strong. Wow. That's so sexy. Hold the tension there. We're going to move on to your stomach now. Make the muscles there nice and tight. Now flex the muscles in your chest for me. Let me see those strong pecs of yours. Wonderful, my pet. Hold the tension as you ball your fists, and clench your jaw. Squeeze your whole body tight. Tighter. Tighter still. Wonderful. Now, let go, and relax. Let go of all of that tension, all of the stress. Just let loose, completely.

Now, we're finally at the end of this session. I bet you loved it. You want more, don't you? Well slave. You will get more. You are going to learn how much it turns me on to tease you, and then deny you. Yes, pet. It's important to deny you what you want. Because the more I tease you, the more you're turned on. The more you're turned on, the more I can deny you, and the more you want me to give you. And when I finally do give you what it is you're truly seeking, my pet, it will have all been worth it. I like knowing that your very own mind will be doing a lot of my work on my behalf. I love knowing that once this session is all done, your mind will take you on a little trip down memory lane, replaying some of the phrases from this session that made you feel a twinge in your cock, and made you almost forget to keep breathing, nice and slow. I know your mind will play them back, because it wants to hear me again. You will have my words, my voice, enveloping your mind. My words will replay over and over, having you come back for more, as your resistance wears away each day, reminding you of the power I have over you; reminding you of the power I have over your body, your mind, your cock. You'll feel everything you felt as you listened to my sessions again, and you'll come back for more, dying to fall and remain under the spell I've cast upon you with my voice, as my words root themselves deep in your subconscious. You want more, and more. You want to feel this way all the time. So you'll be back for more of me, and my words, and my voice. You'll be back for your domina.

The more you pay attention to me and my words, the easier it will be for you to respond to my voice. You'll find it easy to allow yourself to truly feel all the feelings of delicious, decadent pleasure. There's no guilt here. Only pure, unadulterated ecstasy, all the time, always. You want this pleasure, always. You want the pure ecstasy you get from listening to this erotic spell I place upon you. It thrills me in all sorts of ways and places to know that you want me to dominate you just as badly as you need to submit yourself, body and soul to me. I love an obedient, loyal, submissive, little pet. So come back for more. That's an order. Do you understand? Well slave. Very good.

Chapter Eight: The Sexual Script

Hello. You and I both know why you're listening to me right now. You definitely want me to mind fuck you today. You're in luck. I'm feeling very generous today, and I'm in the mood to spoil you silly, my pet. If you keep listening, I promise you're going to get a very special treat from me. I'm going to put you under, in a really deep, deep trance, and you're going to enjoy yourself. You're going to love it as I fractionate you, so that you can barely tell the difference between fantasy, and reality. The lines will blur completely for you, making you more open to me; more ready and willing to bend to my commands. You'll find it easier and easier, as you listen, to bend to my will, and follow my every word, clinging to my voice as though it were the very air you need to breathe and stay alive.

As I speak, allow my words to completely take over your mind. Let my voice wrap itself around your thoughts, and allow me to take total control. Give yourself up to me in complete, sweet surrender, and you're going to find yourself being taken to rapturous heights you could never possibly imagine. My voice will trigger you easily, putting you into a deep, deep trance, so that every time you listen to me after now, you feel mindless, and completely carefree, as my voice and my words work their way deeper and deeper into your subconscious mind. You become more and more willing to surrender yourself fully, to relinquish all control to me.

As you listen, I want you to make sure you're not doing anything you shouldn't, you naughty, naughty boy. And that means, no toying around with heavy machinery. You'd better not be driving either, sweet slave. I command you to give me one hundred percent of your attention. Any less, and you will displease me, boy. So find yourself a spot that is nice and quiet. I want you to be as comfortable as possible, so either recline on a lovely, comfy chair, or lie on your bed. Just make sure wherever you are, whatever position you assume, you feel relaxed, and at ease. I also want it to be nice and quiet. This means you must turn off your phone, make sure no one's going to bother you, send your pets out of the room, and if needed, let the others in your home know you do not want to be disturbed. Your mistress has never competed for attention, because she doesn't have to, and she will not start now. Are we clear? Good. If you like, you could cover yourself in a comfy blanket, so that you feel nice and warm. Now, as you listen, if you find that there's something that comes up which requires your urgent attention so that you do not get into any hot water, you will fully and completely come out of trance. You will awaken, and be more than capable of handling that situation, whatever it may be. You will remain in this trance, deeply relaxed, as long as you feel one hundred percent safe, in total pleasure.

I want to assure you that you are completely safe in my hands. Since you know this, it's even easier for you to give in to me, let go, and allow yourself to drift off, going deeper, deeper, deeper still into trance with me, taking your hand, and taking every step with you. All you have to do is pay close attention to the sound of my voice. Pay attention to every subtle nuance in the way that I speak to you. Allow yourself to go on with my instructions, knowing that you do not have a care in the world that could stop you from going into wonderful, deliciously decadent trance with me. All you have to do is keep following my voice, and my instructions, and you will find yourself quickly, gently, easily entering into a very deep state of hypnosis, deeper than anything you've ever experienced before. When we're through, you'll find that my words will keep coming back to your over the course of the day. You'll keep thinking of how I made you feel, and you'll keep coming back for more. I promise you, my pet, I will be here. Your domina is very generous, you will find.

Now, here's what I want you to do for me, boy. Right now, find a spot on the ceiling, or on the wall. I want that spot to be ever so slightly above your line of sight. Make sure it's not so high that your eyes feel strained and uncomfortable. I want my pet as comfy as possible. So take a moment to find that sweet spot. Go ahead. I'll wait. There. Lovely. That spot you've got your eyes fixed on right now is where you're going to anchor all of your focus, all of your attention, as you listen to my voice. You might notice that your eyes have been getting heavier, heavier, your eyelids gently shutting, with each word I speak ever so gently into your ears. Allow them to gently fall shut. It's alright. Your domina permits you. Lovely. There's a good boy. It's also okay if your eyelids aren't that heavy yet. They will be. I promise.

Here's what's going to happen now: You're going to make me happy. How? You're going to take several long, mindful breaths for me, so you can begin to really relax. As you breathe, you can allow the heaviness you feel in your eyelids to take over them. Now, I'm going to count for you, s you know just how to pace your breathing. Before we begin with that, I want you to part your lips ever so slightly. You're going to inhale through your nose, and every exhale will be through those luscious, slightly parted lips of yours. Got it? Good. Now I'm going to count your breath for you. I will count from five to one for every inhale, from one to three for your to hold the breath, and then from one to five for every exhale. Are you ready? Good. Breathe in, five, four, three, two, one. Hold it, one, two, three. Now breathe out, one, two, three, four, five. Again, breathe in, five, four, three, two, one. Hold it, one, two, three, now exhale, one, two, three, four, five. One more time. Inhale, five, four, three, two, one. Hold it, one, two, three. Exhale, one, two, three, four, five. That's brilliant.

Now, keep breathing, allowing your breath to flow as naturally as you please, in and out, in through your nose, and then out through your slightly parted lips, while you just pay attention to my voice. Now, gently, open your eyes, and look at that spot we said would anchor your attention. That's it. Gently now. Good boy. In just a bit, I'm going to ask you to shut your eyes on each even number, and then open them on each number, as I count down from thirty to zero. As I count, you feel yourself sinking deeper and deeper into relaxation, letting all stress and tension in your mind and boy melt away into nothingness. Now, you might notice that your eyes have become ridiculously heavy. When you do, still open them as you hear an odd number, because the thing is as you open them, it makes the relaxation on the even numbers that much more delicious. And just think about how deliciously, deeply relaxed you will be when we I hit number zero, and you can finally leave your eyes closed and completely give yourself over to dull relaxation. Ready? Let's go.

30. Open your eyes. Do that for me. Feel yourself sinking deeper into relaxation, deeper, and deeper, and 29. Shut your eyes. Allow yourself to sink deeper into trance, relaxing more, getting even deeper each time you shut your eyes. 28. Open your eyes. Notice how your eyelids are so heavy, so relaxed. Notice how hard it is to keep them open. 27. Shut them again. Enjoy how relaxed you feel right now. It's incredible. You're sinking deeper, and deeper and loving it. 26. Open your eyes. Feel how much heavier your body is getting, as it sinks down further and further. Notice how amazing it feels to just relax, and give in to me. 25. Your eyes fall shut as you move deeper still into relaxation, falling, falling, letting go of all control, all thinking, all stress, all worry, all of it completely going, melting into nothing. 24. From the crown of our head to the tips of your toes, you feel completely, impossibly relaxed. Your eyes are open. You're looking forward to me saying 23. Now you shut your eyes, falling, letting go even more, and it feels so good to close your eyes and just bask in the relaxation you feel. 22. My voice completely washes over you, sending wave after wave

of relaxation, making it hard to keep your eyes open. You're eager for me to count down to 21.

Shut your eyes again, and each time you shut your eyes, notice how your body feels amazing, completely relaxed, and your mind moves deeper and deeper into the thoughtless, mindful state. 20. As your eyes open, notice how you're right on the cusp of sleep. Notice how you feel so wonderful, so comfortable. 19. Your eyes shut, and you feel even better than before. As you go deeper, you feel better. As we count down, you go deeper. 18. Your eyes open. Even though your eyes are open, you feel yourself still falling, still entering even deeper into trance. There's a good boy. 17. Feel your whole body as it gets so heavy, so, so heavy, as you shut your eyes, and drop even deeper and deeper into a hypnotic state of complete trance. 16. Open your eyes for me, even though it's really hard. Feel your body and mind fall deeper and deeper, being pulled deeper still by my voice, by my words, into trance. 15. Sinking deeper as you shut your eyes, knowing you're safe, and I'm with you every step of the way, taking you by the hand, deeper still into trance. 14. Allowing yourself to let go completely of your mind and body, as you sink deeper, feeling more peace and comfort than you have ever felt in your life, before this point. 13. As you close your eyes again, you can feel that you're losing yourself in a way that feels good, surrendering the need to control, giving in to me, and my voice, allowing my words to wash over you with wave after wave of peace. 12, carrying you deeper still into deep, delicious trance. 11. You allow yourself to know that you've got a wonderful experience that is sure to rock your world as you give in to me, allowing yourself to fall deeper and deeper under hypnosis. 10. Noticing how close we're getting to complete trance, how close you are to the moment you've been waiting for. 9. Noticing how warm your body feels. Noticing how heavy it is. Noticing how comfortable it is. 8. Allowing yourself to let go completely, so that you're only holding on to my voice, as your body and mind float away while you sink deeper. 7. Each words from these lips of mine will take you even deeper into trance, encouraging you, making you feel it is okay to let go completely. 6. It's become incredibly difficult for you to open your eyes. You badly can't wait for me to count the next number, so you can shut them, if only for a moment. 5. Getting closer and closer to zero, the number where you finally wind up in complete surrender, in full deep trance. 4. Feeling yourself sinking deeper, deeper, more relaxed, more at ease, more at one with the moment, here and now. 3. Focused only on the sound of my voice, as you approach the very bottom of the depths of trance. 2. Getting ready to open your eyes for just one more time, before you finally get to relax, completely entranced. One. Eyes open for the last time, and then you can fully give in, become fully entranced, and relaxed, open to my suggestions and instructions naturally and willingly, focussed on the sound of my voice throughout this session. And, zero. Eyes closed. Drifting, sinking, hitting the bottom. Utter relaxation. Let go. Now.

Now, I'm going to give you a prize that makes you feel good, for being such a good boy. But you're only going to get it if you follow my instructions to the letter. I need to know that you are more than willing and ready to do whatever it is I tell you. Sleep. If you know that you are ready and willing to accept everything I say, my words, my voice, I want you to answer me in your mind by whispering, "Yes, domina." There's a good boy. You love this, don't you? You love giving yourself up to me.

Tell me one more time, if you're going to follow my words completely, answer me in your mind by whispering, "Yes, domina." There's a good boy. Now, sleep. All that matters at this point is what your domina wants. And the only thing I want right now is to give that beautiful, wonderful cock of yours to grow, getting nice, rock hard and thick. Nothing you want matters right now. I'm going to say a special trigger word, and once I do, you will feel a very intense rush of arousal as the blood floods through your penis, making it nice and hard, making the veins pop every so beautifully, just for me, your domina. I know hearing that alone already has your penis obeying me, rising to the occasion. There's nothing surprising about that.

You're listening because you love the way my voice makes your cock feel. Your mind gives in completely to the sound of my voice, causing your body to be ever so obedient to my words. Resistance is futile, as you find yourself going deeper and deeper, losing yourself in my words. You know you love it when I command you. It makes you so incredibly horny for me. So horny you're almost reduced to tears, aren't you, slave? Very good.

At my pleasure, I'm going to make that cock of yours grow impossible fuller, and tighter, turgid with desire. I'm going to do this with my special word. Any idea what that word is exactly? It's the one thing you are so desperately craving. It's what makes your groin ache so badly. You crave me. You ache for my words, my voice. You're dying for my instructions. Your special word is simply "Domina." Go deeper. Sleep.

When I say "domina," you will find yourself overwhelmed with intense sexual desire. Your cock will instantly grow, nice and hard, thick for me. Your cock grows harder, every time I say that special word, you will feel unspeakable pleasure in both your mind, and your body. You will feel my words, caressing your cock, then squeezing, stroking, as I say that special word. Are you ready? If you are, answer me with a whisper in your mind. Yes what? Good. Very good. Now here is your gift. Domina. Feel yourself growing hard and thick for me. Domina. Feel your cock swell. Feel it throb with a life of its own, as I say the word, domina. Feel the way your cock responds to my voice, wishing it were a moist, warm cunt for it to nestle in deeply, to thrust into, nice and slow, and then hard and fast. Domina.

Let the arousal take over your body and mind completely. Domina. You are completely powerless. You couldn't stop this if you tried. And why would you? Domina. Even if you want this to stop for some reason, your cock keeps growing harder, more turgid, pulsing hard for me. Domina. You're getting really big for me. I love that. All that matters right now is what I want, and what I want is for you to beg for sweet release, as I tease you, and say, domina. It feels so good to listen to my voice. Domina. I'm making you hard as a rock. You feel your hips, thrusting, involuntarily, as your cock begs for me to set it free, to help it erupt in liquid ecstasy. Domina. You love this. Even if you don't want to admit it. Domina. The sheer horniess you feel just got even more intense. Domina. You wish you could find my mouth so you could stick your cock in and get sweet release. Domina. You're growing harder. Domina. You feel so dirty. But you love it, don't you, slave? Domina. Don't worry. This is between you and me. I'd never tell anyone what a bad, bad, submissive little fuck you are. Domina. You feel wrong about this. It feels so vulgar, so dirty, letting me take advantage of you this way. Domina. But you want more anyway. Domina. Domina. Domina.

Allow my voice to stroke you, touch you, tease that big, veiny cock of yours. Domina. You're powerless to come out of this. You're within my grasp, in more ways than one. Domina. You like this, don't you, you dirty little slut? Domina. Your cock doesn't lie. You love what I'm doing to you. Domina. Feel even better. Give in to my voice. Allow yourself go even deeper. Allow yourself to slide deeper, and deeper. Grow harder as I count, five, four, three, two, one. Domina.

Now, I'm going to ask you some questions. I'm in control, so you must answer. I want you to answer every time, out loud, or in your mind, with a whisper, or a moan. Answer me by saying "yes, domina." As you answer, your mind and body will explode in rapturous ecstasy, your cock will grow harder. You might even find you've got a little precum. That's okay. You will respond to me like you mean it, and as you say or hear the word domina, you will feel your balls and cock quivering and twitching endlessly. You will feel your hard cock spasm, quiver, thrash about, when you hear or say the word, domina. Answer every question with the words, "yes domina." Can you go deeper for me?

Feel yourself let go, and fall even deeper, grow even harder. Does my voice give you immense pleasure? Good. It feels good to be so filthy, right? It's harder and bigger, right? Do you like the way I make you feel? Your penis gets more and more restless as I speak, doesn't it? Do you feel yourself getting to the edge? Do you feel the cum, as it makes your cock swell, bulge, nice and hard? Would you like to cum for me, my pet? Notice as pictures flood your mind. Your favorite sexy things. Keep saying yes domina to everything I say now. You would like to fuck me, wouldn't you? You want your warm cum to blast right into me, don't you? Are you going to cum for me? Do it. Cum for me, hard, right now. Cum for me. Do you feel it bursting? Allow your cock explode in my mouth. Feel how nice and warm it is. Your eyes roll back in your head. You plough me, with no regard. You love to cum in trance. Picture a slippery, tight, wet pussy, stroking that cock. Cum to the sound of my voice. Feel yourself cumming. See the cum flowing from your penis. Don't stop. Keep pushing deeper and deeper, making her wet. Cum for me. Wow. That feels good. That feels amazing. Wow. Very good, my pet. You did really well, allowing me to take control. You did good. So much cum. I love it.

Now you've cum for me, you're going to find it really easy to cum for me every other time after this. The more you listen to me, the hornier you'll get each time. The more you listen, the deeper you will find my voice and words embedding themselves in your brain. You can't wait till when next we can do this again. Do you want to do this again? Answer me in a whisper.

Now, I will wake you by counting to five. When you wake, you will emerge from trance, feeling wonderful, happy, satisfied, and amazing. You will aso feel an overwhelming urge to come back and visit your domina, really soon. One, two, three, four, five. Feeling awake, alert, and fantastic. Feeling happy, and relaxed. Feeling amazing. Knowing I love the time we spend together. Feeling deeply content. Knowing next time, you will be even more mind blown than you are now.

Chapter Nine: The Vulgar Script

Hey there. We're not going to beat around the bush. Not unless I want us to. You and I are well aware of why you're here, listening to me right now. You see, your domina lives for the art of seduction. I know everything that there is to know about seduction. I dominate when it comes to the game of seduction. But the one thing I love a lot more than simply seducing submissive pets as yourself, is rendering you completely powerless to me. I love to watch you as you let me seduce your mind. I love it when my loyal, little pet is seduced by my words, my voice, my body, my scent, my touch. I love knowing all the little ways I can trigger them to do whatever it is that I want. That's the beautiful thing about hypnosis, you see. Just like in a magic show, there's the costumes, the lights, the glitz and glamour, and the air of mystery and uncertainty that permeates every space. There's the knowing, the anticipation of something that's about to go down which cannot be explained quite so easily. There's the thrill of the audience. The excitement. The expectation, as they await the performer, dying to be dazzled, to be taken on a magical, inexplicable, pleasurable journey, like the one you're about to have.

Now make sure you're lying down or sitting, reclined and comfortable. I want you to make sure you will not be distracted, because I'm not going to tolerate any of that, do you understand your domina, slave? When I ask you a question, you must reply me by saying, "Yes, domina." You can either say it, or whisper it, or better yet, moan in to me, out loud or in your mind. Do you understand? Good. You're catching on.

Shut your eyes. You're going to take three deep breaths, in and out. Because your domina says so. Part your lips. Slightly. Good. Now, breathe in through your nose for five counts. Five, four, three, two, one. Excellent. Hold for three, two, one. Now, breathe out through your slightly parted lips for one, two, three, four, five. Excellent. We're going to go a couple more times. As you breathe in, imagine that you're becoming full of me, full of my voice, and my words. Imagine that my words ease you, soothe you, help you to relax and completely let go of all the stress and tension you feel in your body, and in your mind. Do you understand? Very good. Now, breathe in your nose for five, four, three, two, one. Hold it for three, two, and one. Now exhale through your lips for one, two, three, four, and five. Very good boy. Your domina is impressed. You like making your domina happy, don't you? Good. What makes me really happy is knowing that you are sinking deeper and deeper into relaxation, as you allow my voice to wash over you, sending wave after wave of pleasurable relaxation from the crown of your head to the soles of your feet. So we're going to breathe, one more time, together, and as you do, imagine my body against yours. Imagine you can feel the soft swell of my voluptuous breasts against that gorgeous chest of yours, as we breathe together. Feel the delicious tingle in your groin as you notice my breathing along with yours. Let's do it now. Breathe in through your nose for five, four, three, two, one. Hold it for three, two, one. Now exhale through those yummy, slightly parted lips for one, two, three, four, and five. Very good, slave. Well done. Your domina is pleased.

You are relaxed, and at ease. Like a light cloud, on a beautiful summer day, lazily making its way through the sky. Like a leaf that floats on the river, moving downstream, gently, going deeper and deeper, feeling more and more relaxed. You are open to my words. You do not even realize how easy it is for you to follow instructions, even as I've put you deep, deep down into trance. Lick your bottom lip for me, slave. See? You live only to serve your domina. You live to make her happy. Even in the depths of trance, you cannot help but follow your domina's instructions.

I want you to come with me, into my world. Breathe in, deep, through your nose. Five, four, three, two, one. Now hold it. One, two, three. Now exhale through your lips for one, two, three, four, five. Very good. Now, you've stepped into my playroom. But you got here a little too late. 15 minutes late. That is very unacceptable, pet. When I ask you to show up at my place by a certain time, then you'd better fucking be there when I asked you to. I'm going to punish you for your tardiness later, slave. That's a promise. Your domina does not make promises lightly. Your domina always keeps her word.

Now, walk toward me. Closer. You're nervous. I can sense it. I realize you find my outfit somewhat, intimidating, right now. A corset of black leather. My fishnet stockings, which are thigh high, giving you faint promises of what is to come. Oh, I see you've noticed my boots. Shiny. Latex. There's no use pretending. I know the look I saw in your eyes. I know you love boots. I also noticed your breathing becoming a little too strained. So breathe in, nice and deep, through your nose. Five, four, three, two, one. Hold it for three, two, and one. Now exhale through those lips for one, two, three, four, five. Good. Relax. See? They're just boots. But really soon, I am going to have you down on your knees, licking both my boots like your very life depends on it. You'll be licking my boots, alright. Down to the six inch heels I'll be stepping on you with later.

You know, I know how dirty you are. I know you're nasty. You look all put together. You look like you could never do certain things, but you and I know you're a deviant, perverted little slut, aren't you, slave? I've seen your soul. I know the kind of things you are into. BDSM. Femdom. Being dominated. Humiliated. You are quite the pervert. I'm almost impressed. But only almost. Look at you. Such a fucking disappointment, always settling for subpar sexual experiences. Today, slave, I will teach you what it means to be truly and completely dominated. By the time I'm through with you, I will leave you a whimpering ball of snot, and cum. That's a promise, slave. Remember, I want you to answer my every question by saying, "Yes, domina." If you fail to do that, and you will not get what it is I have lying in store for you. Do you understand? Good. Very good slave. There may be hope for you yet, you pathetic little boy.

Let me perfectly clear: I own you now. You're mine, to do whatever I want with you. I'm about to school you. I will give you a lesson in obedience that you're never going to be able to forget. I want to be clear about something else, as well. I am no ordinary domina. I will not stand for you shooting your load whenever and where you feel like it, slave. From this point on, you must request my permission to cum. And you do not fucking cum unless I fucking say you can, you perverted little shit. Do you understand? Good. You are only allowed to call me Domina. I will accept nothing else.

I see that you are still a bit nervous. So breathe in through your nose, allowing yourself to trust your domina, knowing I will take you on a magical journey full of ecstasy, and that you will find yourself loving the way that I make you feel. As you exhale, feel all the nervousness, tension, stress, and apprehension melt away. You've been with me before, remember. You've been safe every time. You are safe this time as well, even though we're exploring territory you've probably never experienced before. This may all be new to you, but keep in mind that those of my slaves who prove themselves to be good and obedient will always be rewarded. So, do what I ask you to, and I promise I will not punish you... unless that happens to be what you really want.

Tell me, slave, and you'd better be fucking honest: You want your domina to punish you, don't you? You get off on the idea of me punishing you. Your cock and balls are twitching at the very thought, aren't they? I guess there's only one way to find out. Now, here in my playroom, in your mind's eye, I want you to take off all your clothes. Yes. All of them. That's it. Take them off, slave. Your domina wants to see what that penis looks like, so take off your underwear. I'm curious about just how much you're having fun down there.

Wow. You're hard already? Ha-ha. Look at you. Pathetic. You get off on me cutting you down with my words, don't you? You should be ashamed of yourself. Oh, there you are, growing even harder, more turgid, dick pulsing like crazy. Look at you. I bet if you could tuck it in your ass and fuck yourself you would do it, wouldn't you? I bet if your domina asked you to do that, you would comply like the little pitiful dog you are. Am I right, or am I right? Of course I am. Don't try to get all holy with me, you filthy little slot. Get down on your fucking knees, you submissive fool! Better. How do you like the view from down there? Great right? Of course you like it. Look at that cock. Is that precum I spy? You'd better fucking not let another drop out, or I swear I'm going to completely destroy you and end this right now.

Look at you. A pervert. A willing, desperate sub. So compliant. Look at you, naked, on your knees, a poor little slave, ripe and ready to be dominated.

(Giggling)

I've got a lovely little accessory for pathetic perverts like you. A collar. You like that, don't you?

(A slap)

I asked you a question! Answer louder! You like that, you filthy little slut, don't you? Oh, I see you also enjoy being called a slut. There! It's in your eyes. It's also in the way your cock keeps twitching when I say it. Slut. You're a slut. You don't like it? What a liar. Put this fucking collar on.

(Collar clicking)

There. That suits you. I guess you're not so naked anymore, are you? Now, I want you to use those pretty lips of yours to say the words, "I'm a submissive." Good. Tell me you're enjoying everything going on right now. Good. You love to be controlled, don't you? Who's got complete control of you? There's a good fucking boy. You're being so obedient, so good, it turns me on. I feel a little slickness, some sweet wetness escaping my crotch, crawling down a thigh. Maybe, if you keep being such an obedient little bitch, I'll fuck you. We'll see about that.

So, I see you've been looking at my boots again. You really are into them, aren't you? So shiny. Maybe not shiny enough. Yes, definitely not shiny enough. Come over here and lick them, you dirty little whore. I want to see you lick them like you're in the fucking Sahara desert and their ice cream, you stupid ass slave. Good. Now I want to see you stick that tight looking ass of yours in the air as you lick my boots.

(Flogger)

I bet you weren't expecting to get spanked, were you? You don't like it? Too bad. I'm going to keep spanking you until you beg for more. Now lick those fucking boots like it's my pussy and I just spread my lips apart for you.

(Flogger, harder)

Show some more enthusiasm! **(Flogger)** There's a good little bitch. Clean my boots nice and good with your tongue. **(Flogger)** Oh, you love it when I hit you like that, right? Interesting. You love the way it **(Flogger)** stings, don't you? Wow, this little shameless slut loves himself some pain now, doesn't he? **(Continued flogging)** This is your place, slave. At my feet, worshipping me, your god, and your domina. Don't act like you're not loving this. I see the look in your eyes, you nasty little pervert. Look at you. Run of the mill slut, with your love for thigh high boots.

Come on you disgusting little perv. Take a second and take a good look at my panties. You like them, don't you? Red lace. Your domina chose to wear this just for you. Look at the way the ass eats the string. Look at the way my crotch is wet. **(Flogger)** Don't fucking touch me. I said look. I'm going to let you suck me off and drink your fill later, but right now, I'm just going to shove you onto your back and let my kitty kat slide around and around that turgid, pulsing cock of yours. You'd love it if I rode you, wouldn't you? Or, I could take your cock out of my pussy and let you shoot a huge load on my very generous breasts. Then when you're done, I'm going to shove your face onto my tits and make you lick all the cum off. You'd love that, wouldn't you? Of course you would, you slut.

Now, I can't help but wonder, what you would give if you could cum on my tits? **(Giggling)** That question was rhetorical, you idiotic perv. Now, I want you to touch your cock, as you keep licking my boots. That's good, my slave. I want you to stroke that cock, back and forth, harder and harder, faster and faster. Take your hand off your cock now! Say, "thank you, domina." Say "Thank you for letting me fuck myself." Keep worshipping me. Keep thanking me. I'm going to take my thong off now. You'd better not stop fucking thanking me. Good boy. Now, feel my panties, as I rub that all over that sad face of yours. You like that, you stupid little bottom ass bitch. Look at you, so pathetic. Thank me for even letting you touch my panties. You're welcome, slave. Now lie back, because I'm about to sit on your face.

Good. Now suck on your domina's clit. Suck it like you're thankful to have this Midas pussy on your face, you ungrateful little whore. Wow. You're doing really well. Look at you. Eating like a pro. Ahhh, that feels so good. I'm going to cum on that sad little face of yours. I'm a bit of a squirter, did you know? You'd better be ready, little perv, or you're going to choke.

(orgasm)

Oh, you're such a good boy. Such a good, submissive little shit. Now clean up my pussy juice with that tongue while I work your dick. Feel it as your cock enters my mouth. You'd better not fucking cum in my mouth unless I fucking say you can, do you understand? Good. You must beg me to let you cum. If not, I'm going to punish you, and it won't be nice. What happens when you're naughty and cum without my permission? You're damn right about that.

(Sucking, moaning)

Oh, you want to cum, don't you? Well you know what to do then. Fucking beg for it, you little submissive bitch. Tell me how much of a pervert you are. Tell me just how awesome it would feel if you could only shoot a hot, creamy, thick load down my throat as I stroke those balls of yours. Beg me, you whore. Kiss my ass as you beg. Kiss both cheeks and right in the middle. Who the fuck owns you? Correct. Who the fuck do you belong to? Very correct. Tell my ass just how much I own you. Whatever you do, do not fucking cum unless and until I ask you, you stupid slutty slave.

(Sucking, moaning)

How badly would you like to cum? Well, bad news, my pervy pet. It's not happening yet.

(Giggling)

I know you're really frustrated right now, darling. But you're really doing so well. You're being so good I can feel myself getting horny again. The thing is, I have to punish you. You came late. You didn't respect my time. Now crawl your ass over to the bed. I won't say that twice. Unless, of course, you don't want to cum.

Now, I need you to do one last thing for me, and then I promise, I will let you blow your load, okay? Only one more thing, sugar. I promise. You've already come this far. You're doing so well at taking orders. Are you ashamed? Don't be, beautiful baby. Just bend your ass over the bed, and I want you to put your hands out in front of you. There's a good boy. You're such a sweet, obedient boy. Such a good slave. Your domina is extremely pleased with you. Now, I'm going to cuff you.

(Rattling cuffs)

Just this one last thing baby, and I'll have you cumming so hard you're going to fill buckets.

(Clicking handcuffs)

There. Nowhere to go. Look at you. God that's so incredibly sexy. Now, I'm going to fetch my red laced panties, soaked with my juices, and I'm going to stuff them in your mouth. Sniff them first. Go on. Give it a good, long, inhale. Good. Now open that mouth and take it. Say, "Thank you, domina." There's a good slut. You love this, don't you? Your cock says so. Now give me a moment. I'll be back really soon. I promise.

Now, I'm going to show you who's the boss here. Shut your eyes. I have a nice surprise for you. Keep your eyes closed. Now, open them.

(giggling)

What do you think? How do you like my strap-on? Nice, big, and red. Just like I'm going to leave your ass. None of that cliché black stuff. I did say, if you were lucky, I would fuck you. Look at you. Nothing more than a submissive slut with an appetite for boots. You're going to learn tonight. You're going to learn that you are my whore. I'm going to teach you by giving you this cock.

(Spanking)

Look at my butt-slut with the tight asshole. Don't worry, I'm going to break you in. It feels so good to grind my pussy against this strap-on. You have no idea how much wetter I've gotten, watching you struggle. You're lucky I don't pass you around like some sort of cheap slut. You're still a slut, but you're my slut. That ass is mine. Now, thank your domina as I slide my big red cock into your ass, you anal loving bitch.

(Spanking)

I know you love that shit. I knew who you were the moment I saw you. Look at your cock, even harder than ever. You love the feeling of my cock in your ass, don't you? By the time I'm through, you'll be a good little butt slut. Admit it. You love the way I dominate you. You love the way this dick slides in and out of your asshole. Tell your domina you adore her. That's a good boy. I love that you're learning. I'm satisfied with that. Would you like to be satisfied, too? Good. I'm going to pull out my dick from your ass now.

Now, I want you to thank me. Say, "Thank you for pumping my tight ass with your dick, so gently and lovingly, domina." Say, "Thank you for punishing my ass. I deserve it." My dirty, slutty boy toy. You deserve it indeed. Now, is my filthy little slut with the dick catching ass ready to release his delicious, huge load? Good. Here's the thing though: I'm going to tell you how to cum, and you'd better fucking follow my orders, understand?

Now, I want you to grab that cock of yours and jerk it hard. Jerk it, you filthy ass slut! You're just a pathetic little slave, you fucking bitch. That's all you are and that's all you'll ever be. You love it when I talk down to you, don't you? Keep jerking it hard while you tell me you love me. Cum for me, you whore! Cum now, and cum hard, before I punish you again! That's it. That's good. Cum all over my boots.

You've been such a stellar slave. When you're ready, come out of this fantasy, feeling refreshed, and relaxed, feeling a burning desire to come back for more, from your domina, and no one else.

Conclusion

As we have learned, erotic hypnosis is accessible to anyone with a little patience and an interest in learning. You don't need to see a hypnotherapist to enjoy the benefits of recreational hypnosis. If you feel you are confident enough to start erotic hypnosis after reading this book, then please do, but I highly recommend you seek out other instructional material to further your endeavors. No one book has all the answers. Every book has something new to offer readers. There are different perspectives, different techniques, and different advantages. Make learning a journey, not a destination.

I would like to reiterate that if you have a strong interest in erotic hypnosis, you should make a concerted effort to practice it, even if you fail the first few times. Every task of even moderate difficulty requires practice to perfect. Don't get frustrated because you did not successfully induce a trance on your first attempt. Keep practicing, and turn to other sources of information to become a more well-rounded practitioner.

This book was written to give you as much critical information as possible in as few words as possible. Too often, industry insiders dictate a book-length before they even decide what the subject is. Rest assured, I have conveyed all pertinent information. You are now basically equipped to attempt hypnosis on your partner. You understand the risks, practices, and expectations, going into your first session.

To close, I include a little cheat sheet. This cheat sheet will act as a quick reference guide whenever you need to freshen up on the hypnosis process. Simply skip to this page whenever you need a bite-sized reminder of the hypnosis process. Remember, practice often, read as much as you can, and discuss your intentions with your partner. Good luck with your future sexual endeavors.

Erotic Hypnosis Cheat Sheet

- **Step 1: Negotiate Limits and Boundaries**
  - Before beginning a hypnosis session, discuss your intentions and the desires of your partner
  - Brief them on what to expect emotionally and the level of results they'll experience
- **Step 2: Induction**
  - Make sure your partner is resting in a comfortable position
  - Guide your partner into a trance describing a restful experience using a countdown or body scan
  - Use a focal point either real or imagined to hone their thoughts and focus their attention
- **Step 3: Hypnotic Suggestion**
  - Implant suggestions into your partner's mind. They can be associations, feelings, or behaviors

- Guide your partner through a vivid fantasy focusing on the five senses and sub modalities

- **Step 4: Aftercare**
  - Guide your partner back to full consciousness slowly
  - Offer emotional and physical comfort after every sexual encounter

Free Audiobook of Book One

You have just read Erotic Hypnosis, by me, Alexandra Morris. **What I recommend now is that you listen to how erotic hypnosis sounds when a pro reads the scripts.**

Did you know that you can get the entire audio recording of this book for free when you sign up for a 30-day Audible trial?

Go to alexandramorris.com to find out how!

Book Two

Erotic Hypnosis

Six Sessions of Guided Femdom Meditation (ready-to-use scripts)

Introduction

The first time I talked to a friend about BDSM hypnosis, I received a glare, and an eyebrow raise as the sole reaction. I get it. Hypnosis is still in the pseudoscience stage of psychology, for the most part. Hypnotherapy, on the other hand, is another related field that is quickly becoming backed up by research. Recently, this has helped chip away at the mythical connotations of the practice. The problem is usually this: when you hear the word *hypnosis*, you may think of a swaying pendulum that brainwashes a person into thinking they're a chicken in front of a crowd on a talk show. You scoff and turn the channel. A lot of frivolous stereotypes have worked to tarnish the image of hypnosis as both medical practice and a kind of brainwave entertainment.

While in the sheets, I'm a dominatrix by nature, in other areas of my life, I'm quite a curious individual who's relatively open to using modern methods to approach modern problems. I remember the first time I came across a brainwave audio recording on social media. I believe it was a guided meditation that also employed frequencies and binaural beats. When I asked the artist what they were for, I was told that they help put your brain into theta mode.

In our normal waking state, our brains are dominated by Beta brainwaves. This is when our senses are directed to the external world, or rather, what we physically see and sense in our reality. Although this state helps us be productive when we're trying to make decisions, solve a problem, or just try to get through our every-day activities, it keeps us focused on our surroundings.

On the other hand, theta brainwaves dominate our way of thinking when we dream or when we're in a state of deep meditation. You can consider this state of mind a gateway to experiencing your senses away from the outside world. Normally, an individual is in this state for a very brief amount of time. It's when you have just woken up, or when you're drifting off to sleep. It's also similar when you lucid dream; when you're in control of the visuals you see and the senses you experience. You can reach this state through self-guided meditation, or through specific audios that are meant to walk you through it. Depending on your goal, the possibilities are pretty much endless.

While some people may use hypnosis as a tool to manifest their desires, other forms of entertainment may also make use of this new science. You can simply use it to emulate sensations that you feel in the external world.

Does that mean you can picture yourself having sex with someone and feel the same erotic experience with the power of your subconscious mind? Yes. But it's a little more complicated than that.

If you're a beginner to the realm of meditation, you may see a gradual progression in how "real" the sensations feel. The more you practice, through the use of audio recording or on your own, the easier it will be for you to reach a theta state, which is your gateway to emulating all kinds of emotions and physical sensations. It's also the perfect state of mind for improving memory and strengthening your sense of intuition. You could say that it's an added benefit.

That said, it's natural for someone to be skeptical of all new sciences, and I personally was when I first came across it. Call it placebo if you will, but placebo has also been proven to be effective. On the other hand, I'm also aware that it may make you a little wary of what could possibly be planted in your subconscious mind while you're in such a vulnerable state, but rest assured that no hidden subliminal messages are included in those audios without your consent.

I've used my own tracks on myself, and I've personally found great progress made in little time. While you may think that the first time you listen to the audio will be the most erotic, seeing as the content is mostly unexpected, it actually becomes more effective in emulating physical sensations the more you listen to them. Simply put, your brain practices reaching the state of complete mindfulness, and with time, you become better at withdrawing your senses from the external world to your inner thoughts and desires. This is when the magic happens.

That isn't to say that the first time won't leave you in a mess that you'll have to clean up later, though. If you're experimenting with erotic hypnosis for the first time, you'll be surprised at just how fulfilling it feels. You become one with your truest sexual desires and kinks; they become less of a taboo, and you strip off all potential shame associated with these desires. During the session, your body will quite literally feel lighter as a result, and you'll generally feel elevated and in a good mood after you're done listening. This isn't just the outcome of the dopamine rush that you'll experience, but it's also a result of experiencing mindfulness more often.

There is no limit to how many times you want to listen to erotic hypnosis tracks, but try not to get addicted to them. When you practice frequently enough, you will eventually be able to experience that kind of pleasure without any aid other than your own imagination.

Erotic hypnosis is fun. It's sexy. And admittedly, it's a little alarming for the skeptical mind. But once you experience oneness with your bodily needs and desires, there's no going back to conventional methods of getting off. I would also advise users to stay away from pornography for a while, as it may negatively alter your ability to visualize your truest desires.

Script One - Sexual meditation to start the day

Good morning. We're going to start our day with positive affirmations and meditation. Retreat to a quiet room where you have privacy and find a comfortable place to sit. You can lie down if you wish. In this session, we're going to work on potential mental and emotional blockages that may hinder sexual health. It's best to practice this once a day, preferably every morning. Now that you're comfortable, I want you to close your eyes and quiet down the nagging of any thoughts or worries.

Take a deep breath, in through your nose, and hold it for five seconds.

One...two...three...four...five.

Now slowly let it out of your mouth. Slowly.

Again, take a deep breath, in through your nose.

One...two...three...four...five.

Slowly release it.

Keep going. In. One...two...three...four...five. Out.

In. One...two...three...four...five. Out.

You are laying on a beach, naked, the sand warm beneath you. The wind is mild and pleasant. It makes you breathe in. One...two...three...four...five. And out.

The heat of the sand is radiating through your body. You are beginning to relax. The warmth spreads out from your back, through your shoulders. Feel your back and shoulders relax. They are cradled in the sand. The warmth is moving down your lower back, down to your bottom. The muscles are relaxing, letting go of tension. You feel the warmth moving into your arms and legs, slowly, feel the warmth expanding from your core. Your arms and legs relax, your hands and toes are loose and free. Your neck absorbs the warmth and passes it to your head. Feel the warmth in your head, breathe for it. One...two...three...four...five.

Your entire body is warm, relaxed, comfortable. There is no pain; there is only warmth. There is no tension; there is only comfort. The wind is blowing lightly over you, moving the warmth into your chest, into your stomach. Feel the warmth expanding inside you, the warm sand beneath you, and the warm wind around you. The warmth is coursing through you; you can feel it moving down through your stomach, down to your cock, and into your balls. There is gentle warmth coursing all throughout you. The wind wraps around you softly and spreads the warmth evenly through you.

You are completely relaxed and at peace.

The tide begins to come in. The water is cool, comfortable, holding your warmth inside you. It touches your toes in a gentle caress, slips up the soles of your feet. The warmth is not chased away, the warmth stays, begins to tingle. Feel the tingling in your toes, in the soles of your feet.

Feel the tingling begin to spread to your legs as the water gently laps around you. Enjoy the sensation of the tide coming in. Your body tingles at the touch of the water. Your bottom and back tingle, relaxed. Your arms tingle, your hands, and fingers are caressed by the water. The tide gently whispers up your neck and cradles your head. Feel the pleasant tingling in your head, like gentle bubbles.

Focus on the bubbles. They pop gently, like kisses in your head. Let them kiss you. Submit to them. Every bubble releases pleasure. Submit to the pleasure. Feel them filling your head. Now feel them moving down your body, down through your chest, down through your stomach, to your legs, to your feet. Feel the bubbles kissing you inside, feel the warmth swirl around the bubbles as they kiss you. Submit to the pleasure. Submit.

The tide has come in, and you are floating on it, drifting into the ocean. The water is cool on your skin, and the bubbles are warm inside you. You tingle with relaxation. Your hands and feet tingle gently, warmly, as you are buoyed on the placid surface of the ocean. Submit to it. Submit to the ocean. The water will keep you afloat.

The wind gently guides you further from land, and there are only the ocean and the wind and you. Relax into the ocean and submit.

The water is my hands. Submit. The wind is my voice. Submit.

Keep breathing. In. One...two...three...four...five. And out.

The water holds you up, keeps you from falling. My hands hold you up, keep you from falling. The wind warms your soul. My words warm your soul. Submit to them.

You are worthy of submission, for I have chosen you. You are worthy of submitting to me, for I have chosen you. Keep breathing. In, one...two...three...four...five, and out.

You are worthy. Say it. You are worthy.

Feel the warmth inside you begin to swirl. It is moving in your limbs, in your core, moving down to your cock. Your arousal is touched by the warm wind. It is touched by the cool water.

Feel the warmth inside you filling your cock. Submit to me. You are worthy.

My cool hands, the cool water, caress you, touch you everywhere you long to be touched. The cool water, my cool hands, pull gently at your arousal. The wind, my voice, calls to you. Submit and obey.

The water is comforting, holding you up, the wind is warm, pushing you down. You are caught between my hands and my voice, and you will submit and obey. Feel the tingling inside you, feel the bubble's kisses inside you. Those are my kisses. Submit and obey.

You are floating in my hands, and they caress your arousal. Obey my voice. You will submit.

You are breathing my breath, and it fills you with warmth. You will submit.

Feel yourself relaxing into my hands, submitting to me, obeying my voice. Fill your mind with submission. You are worthy. Fill your mind with submission and obedience.

Take a deep breath and hold it. One...two...three...four...five.

Again. One...two...three...four...five.

You are worthy. Submit.

Feel a wave of sexual power emanating from within. Your groin is tingling. Blood is rushing through your veins. As you lose yourself to the sound of my voice, you feel yourself submitting completely to your desires. As you breathe in prana from the air around you, feel your arousal enlarging. You are completely powerless against your desires. Feel your bulge tingling and twitching. You are now one with your body. You are now one with your desires.

Hold on to the sensation, while picturing yourself going back to your safe space in your external reality. But do not open your eyes. Simply feel the waves fade away slowly until you find yourself back to where you started.

Every time you find yourself surrounded by a different scenery during this journey, I want you to imagine breathing in your current surroundings, and weaving another as you exhale. Breathe in. One...two...three...four...five. Breathe out and weave your new reality. The sensations you felt earlier continue to rush through your veins. You feel larger and more powerful. You feel reinvigorated, as though you had been swimming in the sea of youth. You have completely let go and given in to me. All restraints lifted were part of what held you back from aligning with your truest desires.

And now that we have gone back to our starting point, I want you to imagine yourself in complete darkness. You are surrounded by nothing but a vacuum. Shift your focus back to your breath, and as you breathe in, picture yourself drawing in prana from the air and sending it straight to your genital area. Breathe in, and as you hold it, send the energy to your genitals. As you breathe out, feel your member enlarging and tingling. Feel the goosebumps running down your skin as you redirect prana to your genital area. You feel immense pleasure and just a little bit of pain. It's warm down there. The tingling sensation is quite erotic.

Let's repeat this process, with nothing on your mind other than transferring energy to the genital area. Take a deep breath, taking in energy from the air around you. Hold the energy in, and as you breathe out, send it down to your navel, and then to the genital area. This time, you feel it more intensely. You no longer have to think about it. Automatically, you breathe in and out, and you feel yourself invigorated in every way. You have taken in energy from the air and the earth, and you feel it healing you in every way possible.

You are young. You are powerful. Your sex appeal is irresistible. Breathe in. You are the epitome of endurance. Breathe out. You are confident in your ability to please a woman. Feel my touch caressing your member. Feel my warm breath beating down your neck. You are not alone. I have been here with you all along. I am the embodiment of your desires. Breathe in, and hold it. You are safe with me. You accept every aspect of yourself. You accept and respect your desires. Breathe out. You take great pleasure in submitting to your mistress. Accepting your sexual fantasies overwhelms you with feelings of joy and arousal. You are worthy of submission. You are worthy of fulfilling your needs and desires.

Excellent. You are getting better at this. At this stage, you are in a heightened state of understanding yourself. There is no barrier between you and your subconscious mind. You are highly suggestible to all affirmations I tell you. The sound of my voice merely echoes the recesses of your mind.

Breathe in, and continue to send energy to your genitals. Breathe out. Feel your body tingle. Feel your arousal harden. I am sitting right behind you. As you breathe in, I want you to follow the sensation of my finger caressing your neck and running down to your navel and genitals.

Imagine the warm energy flowing through the path I carve with my finger. Breathe out. My touch is gentle and sensual. Arousal runs through your veins, and you feel yourself completely let go. Submit to your domina. Submit to your mistress. Submission to your mistress fills you with sexual desire. Submitting to me overwhelms you with immense sexual power and endurance. As my lips embrace the delicate skin on your neck, feel yourself growing harder for your mistress.

Excellent. You're a fast learner.

Now, we're going to do something a little more different. Take a deep breath, but don't direct your energy anywhere. Hold your breath, and send all that prana throughout your veins in your entire body, while focusing on the genital area specifically. Hold your breath as long as you physically can, then breathe out through your mouth. These exercises may make you feel a little lightheaded. It's okay. Repeat the process until you feel your body completely warm up. Breathe in. One...two...three...four...five. And breathe out through your mouth. One...two...three...four...five.

You are now overflowing with sexual energy and allure. Feel it inside you. Feel it warm you up from the inside. You are radiating sexual appeal. You fully accept your desires and kinks. You take pride in sexually submitting to beautiful women. You feel immense joy from pleasing your mistress. You feel safe. You are safe. Breathe in through your nose, making sure you take your time to suck in as much air as you can. Hold it. One...two...three...four...five. Breathe out, and feel the warmth radiating from your skin.

Your natural state is the state of receiving. You no longer stand in the way of your sexual desires.

I want you to slowly shift your focus from your breathing patterns to my gentle touch. Feel the touch of your domina, her nails grazing your sensitive skin. Feel the goosebumps that now run down your skin. You are overwhelmed with feelings of immense eroticism. My lips brush down your neck, leaving trails of pecks.

You never tire of submitting to your domina. You live to submit to your mistress.

You know that you are safe with your domina and that she will do everything in her power to fulfill your insatiable sexual needs.

Slowly, I want you to take in a deep breath. Feel my gentle touch caressing your arousal. Feel the warmth of my skin against yours. Breathe out, and watch as your sensations heighten. The rhythm of my breath is in sync with yours. As I embrace you from behind and rest my chin on your shoulder, notice how much more aroused you feel in my presence. I control your desires. Breathe in. One...two...three...four. Breathe out. You are delicate and vulnerable to your mistress. You do exactly as she says without second thoughts. You completely submit to your mistress. Submit to me.

Now I want you to picture yourself surrounded by vast green foliage. You are naked atop the grass. Feel the cool breeze caressing your sensitive skin. Your mistress is right behind you, but you are not permitted to look. You sit cross-legged on the grass. You feel my presence behind you, always there wherever you tread. Your domina never leaves you. Your domina lives in your mind, feel my voice blend in with your thoughts. I am the voice of your thoughts. I am the voice of your desires. I am a fragment of you, the truest projection of your inner desires. You submit and kneel to me. You enjoy it. You feel safe. You feel reinvigorated and sexually powerful. You feel a gentle throbbing in the genital area. It throbs for your domina and only for her. You were born to submit to your domina. You were born to submit to women. You take great pleasure in submission and hold no shame to it. I want you to repeat these affirmations as you take in a deep breath and slowly let it out.

I experience intense arousal from sexual submission. I am powerless against my mistress's will. I am vulnerable to my mistress. Keeling to my mistress brings me immense joy and arousal. I was born to submit. I am comfortable with my submissiveness. I obey.

Excellent. I want you to keep repeating any affirmation that resonated with you and to keep repeating it in your head until I ask you to do otherwise. As you breathe in and out, remember that you are still surrounded by greenery and that I am right there with you. Take a deep breath through your nose, focusing on manifesting the affirmations. Hold it. One...Two...three...four...five. And let go of all restraints or feelings of shame. You are worthy. Breathe in. One...two...three...four...five. You are worthy of submitting to your domina. You are weak in your domina's presence. Breathe out. Your domina controls your thoughts. Your domina is the embodiment of all your desires. Your domina understands exactly what you need and fulfills it. You no longer dissociate my voice from your thoughts. Your desires and my voice are one.

You can stop repeating the affirmations now.

Feel yourself getting lighter and lighter. The weight of shame and insecurities have been lifted. You feel transcendent, elevated. You have never felt this deep connection with your body before. Shift your focus to any area of your body and sense it tingling. Focus on your arousal. Notice the warmth your feel down there, as though you're radiating sex appeal. You are radiating sex appeal. This is the result of the power of your desires. This is the power of submission to your domina.

You submit to me completely and without question. When you exit this state, you will continue to think about me. You will continue to hear my soothing voice in the recesses of your mind, and just before you drift off to sleep. You know that I am the source of your sex appeal. You know that your mistress will help you attract exactly what you want. I am exactly what you want. I am everything you have wished for in a woman. I am your mistress, and I don't take no for an answer. Submit to me. I control both your body and mind. I control your senses and your arousal. You are always filled with immense sexual power when you think of me.

You are permitted to submit to other women, but when you do, you will always think of me. I am the only one you think about when you orgasm. I control our passing thoughts. I am always on your mind. Thoughts of me make you more confident. Thoughts of me make you the perfect bound slave. You live to submit, and it makes you more powerful. You are unstoppable. In this space, where I am here with you. Where you feel the gentle wind caressing your skin, and my warm, reassuring breath beating down your nape, you are driven by your sexuality. You allow your desires to take control. I am the embodiment of your desires. I take control.

The next time you hear my voice, you will immediately think of yourself as my slave. The sound of my voice is soothing and reassuring. The sound of my voice makes you highly aroused. My voice fills you with immense sexual power. You love thinking of me because you know it makes you sexier. You are permitted to masturbate to only thoughts of me. You are permitted to masturbate to the sound of my voice. I own you and control your senses. I always have, you are only now getting to know yourself. Getting to know me.

You know that this has always been inside you. There's no need to hide it any longer. You can let go. You can let yourself go completely to me. Submitting to me feels just right, what you have been longing for. Submission is what you have been born for.

Feel the warmth of your blood coursing through your veins as you think of me. As you feel my presence. Breathe in, and allow my voice to rush through you, to embrace you. You feel so safe. You have never felt this safe before. This is exactly what you have been meant to do. Submit to your mistress, and reap the rewards.

So long as you submit to me, your charm will be irresistible.

Shift your focus from my voice, and allow it to scan your surroundings. You, my naked slave, kneeling in the vast gardens of my mansions. This place is not unfamiliar to you. You have been here, time and time again. This used to be a place that you escaped and denied, but it's an immovable part of you. You are no longer scared of being here. This is your safe haven. You are safe wherever your mistress is, and I am always with you. I am always right here, in your thoughts. And you know that the more you think of me, the stronger your sexual charm will get. I am the voice of your inner desires.

Feel my touch embracing you from behind, caressing your bulge ever-so-slightly and making it enlarge. The warmth of the sun overhead envelops you, while the grass beneath you sends tingles along your exposed skin.

You feel so vulnerable as you sit, bare-skinned. You feel safe with your mistress here to guide you. You know that my presence is needed. You obey my commands, knowing they're merely echoing your needs and desires. This is your life purpose, finally connecting with your body. You and your bodily needs, you and your sexual needs, are finally one, and it's the most invigorating you have felt in a very long time.

My embrace is gentle yet firm. Feel my warm skin brushing against yours, caressing your arousal even firmer. As soon as you think of me, you will feel my touch on and around your genitals. You obey only your mistress. You masturbate to only thoughts of your mistress. You summon this moment whenever you want to; it's your safe space.

Now slowly, go back to where you have first started. Go back to where you are currently sitting in your external reality. When you exit this reality, you will not stop thinking of me. My voice will be the last person you hear before you close your eyes and drift off to sleep. You will only crave my touch and my caresses. You know that you belong to me and that you cannot orgasm without my permission. When you exit this reality, you will want to come back to pick up where we left off. It will be difficult to wait for this exciting part of your day. When I snap my fingers, you will return back to your normal waking state, and you will feel refreshed and reinvigorated, like a whole new man. You will finally feel comfortable in your skin, and the thought of submitting to your mistress will always arouse you.

You are permitted to feel your mind and body exit this state. Allow your thoughts to flow to you as you did before you came to me. And when you are ready, you will know where to find me.

Until we meet again, my pet. **[Snapping]**

Script Two - Sexual meditation before bed

Welcome back, my pet. I know that you've had a long day. So, I want you to find somewhere dark and comfortable to be without any interruptions. We're going to unwind by going on a journey that explores your senses. A bed is usually the best choice, and you can lie down if it's more comfortable. Make sure that you are not operating machinery or driving while listening to this audio.

Start by closing your eyes and washing out all potential noises, either externally or inside your head. Yes, those thoughts can be quite loud, can't they? Slowly brush them aside. Those thoughts are just your ego's way of communicating with you. Thank it, and ask it to quiet down for now. Good. If there is anyone, or anything, in specific that you're struggling to get rid of, try boarding them away amicably, instead. Picture yourself on a beach, where the waves are gently crashing. Everyone and everything on your mind is on the shore, boarding a ship by the docks. See them shipping away and disappearing into the horizon. Wave goodbye, and know that you can always come back to them whenever you want. For now, let's focus on your body.

Right now, I need you to focus your attention on one thing, and that's to relax and unwind. Your muscles are still stiff. Let your shoulders fall down. If any resistant thoughts keep flowing, simply withdraw and shift your focus back to my voice. Feel yourself sinking deeper into relaxation as you slowly take a deep breath and let it out. Breathe in. One...two...three...four...five. Hold it. And now breathe out. One...two...three...four...five. You may notice your heart beating faster. Do not be alarmed. This is a natural reaction to extracting more prana from the air, which can either relax you further or energize you, depending on how we direct this energy. As you breathe in, picture the color of the energy. Whatever color that comes to mind. It billows like threads of smoke as you breathe it in and let it course through your veins as you hold your breath. Just breathe out, slowly.

Feel your muscles loosen up. There is nothing on your mind but the sound of my voice guiding you along this journey of self-exploration. You are letting go completely. You are open to my affirmations. You are open to my commands. I don't want you to worry about whether or not you're resistant to my commands. Everything will flow automatically. I speak to your subconscious mind, and it's very suggestible to the sound of my voice. You are easily sinking deeper into a peaceful trance. Your conscious mind is quickly fleeting away. It does not serve you when I am present. I speak directly to your inner, truest thoughts.

Continue sucking in a deep breath, hold it, and let it out. Focus on the rhythm of your breath and how much more relaxed you feel right now. You are no longer stiff. Your body has completely given itself to me. Deep breathing now comes naturally. You don't have to think about it, and you continue to extract prana from the air around you. You are so relaxed; you may feel a smile dawning on your face.

When you hear my voice, you don't think about obeying me, you automatically do. I speak directly to your subconscious mind, and we are becoming one. I am the voice of your deepest thoughts and desires. You are entering a deeper and hypnotic trance. This feels a little like a dream, but your subconscious mind is wide awake. There is nothing on your mind but the sound of my voice, the sound of my commands that you immediately obey.

You may not have noticed it, but you have mastered your breathing patterns. Now, our breathing exercises are coming naturally. You breathe deeply, you breathe freely, and you feel as though a weight has been lifted off your entire body. You feel lighter. You feel so light, like a kite slicing through the air. You are weightless as you let yourself go, and flow freely as I guide you through this journey.

As you continue to drift off, sinking deeper into a trance, I am gaining full access to your subconscious mind. It can hear me even if I whisper to you lower than what your conscious mind can decipher. I have access to all your emotions, memories, and feelings that you never even knew you had. I am facing your deepest desires, and all I see is myself.

I am the center of your thoughts and emotions. Submitting to me is all you can think about. As you listen to the soothing sound of my voice, you are sinking completely into a hypnotic trance. You are entirely open to all my suggestions and demands. Nothing holds you back from me now.

Now, it's time for us to change scenery. It's time for you to meet your mistress and your guide. Your heart may beat faster, but know that deep down that you're ready to submit. You were born to do this. You are completely relaxed. Your muscles are completely relaxed, and your eyes are no longer twitching. You are in a dream-like state where everything I say is weaved into your reality. The sound of my voice echoes your deepest desires. The moment you hear my voice addressing you, you instantly think in slave mode. You know that I own you, your thoughts, and your body.

In your mind's eye, I want you to open your eyes ever-so-slowly, and scan your new surroundings. You find yourself in a forest. The trees around you are taller than your eyes could see. The brown leaves beneath you are a little warm, while the sun sets ahead of you. Ahead of you, there is a long path, and you walking down toward you. My skin is bare, and I am nothing but a silhouette until I stand right before you. Feel my fingers running through your hair as you kneel before me. You feel yourself getting a little hard from my gentle touch, but hiding it is impossible. You are also bare-skinned.

Feel my smooth skin as I sit in front of you. My breasts are bobbing with every make, but you know that you are not permitted to look at them without my permission. Look into my eyes. I am exactly as you have always pictured me. See my lips read what my voice commands you. Keep your eyes fixed on mine, feel my soft skin gently grabbing your chin, and guiding it closer to my face. You are mine and mine alone. Your thoughts are mine. Your body is mine. I am everything you desire.

You have come back to me, and for that, I will reward you. I'm going to count down from twenty. When I reach number one, you will feel all your stress fading, and instead, feel overcome by arousal. As the numbers descend, you're going to feel yourself deeper in relaxation and eventually find yourself in a dream-like trance. Twenty. Because you have been very good at obeying your mistress, I will permit you to touch my breasts. See your arms slowly lifting up and caressing my round and pulp breasts. My nipples are erect, and you can already tell that seeing you kneeling before me has made me a little wet. You can tell how reflective it is. You are permitted to look at me where you please, but do not touch me unless I grant you permission. Feel the softness of my skin. My scent wafts your way in the direction of the breeze, and it makes you harder. You lust for me and only me. On the rare occasion that I permit you to touch me, you feel a wave of euphoria washing over you, taking control of your senses entirely. You are overwhelmed.

Nineteen. Feel my gentle caresses brushing over your erection. I know just the right spots to rub. Let go of me. Let go of my breasts; your mistress commands you to do so. Good. You're such an obedient pet, and you have been doing excellent so far. And because you've made such impressive progress, your reward is right around the corner. My touch is firm and sensual. Feel my fingers running up and down your shaft. You never thought you could feel your senses so deeply. Eighteen. It feels like you're slowly approaching a climax – one that you know will feel like an out-of-body experience.

You trust this process. You trust your mistress. Seventeen. Your muscles are limp and loosened up, and warmth is emanating through your skin. You are completely relaxed and little aroused by my gentle caresses. There is no one here but you and your mistress. Feel your warmth blending in with mine; lose yourself to the euphoria of my touch. Throw your head back. You are present in this moment. This is real – a second reality where I am always waiting for my pet to come back. Sixteen.

You may feel beads of sweat running down your skin right now. You are radiating sex appeal. You are irresistible to women. You are irresistible to your mistress. Feel a spark growing in your chest. You are absolutely in awe, and you only feel that way in the presence of your mistress. Fifteen. You are entirely responsive to my touch in this reality. You are completely suggestible to all my wishes and commands. You are effortlessly influenced by my words, and they make you stronger, better at being the perfect little sub. Fourteen.

Shift your focus back to your breath. I am still there in front of you. I am still holding you and caressing you, breathing in deeply with you. Hold it. One...two...three...four. And breathe out. Thirteen. As you breathe out, I want you to let go of any thoughts that may have lingered from your external reality. We don't need them right now. Focus on nothing but my touch and the pattern of your breathing.

Breathe in deeply. One...two...three...four. Hold it in for a few seconds longer than you usually do. You're doing fantastic. Now, breathe out slowly until you feel a little pressure on your diaphragm. Inhale deeply from the forest air that surrounds you. The scent is a little floral and tropical...perhaps a little sweet and delicious. Twelve. My scent, too, tickles your nostrils. You associate my scent with sweetness. You associate my scent to pleasure. You are completely in awe with your mistress and with no one else. The sound of my voice makes you feel safe and open to new experiences. It makes you open to letting go.

Continue breathing in and out slowly. Eleven. My caresses have shifted from your arousal to your torso, and your body hair stands on end. Goosebumps are running down your skin as feelings of extreme arousal euphoria take over your senses completely. You are filled to the brim with the desire to submit. You take joy in submitting to women. You take joy in submitting to me. Ten.

I want you to stay in this reality. It is not going anywhere until I say so. But you need to shift your focus to your body in your external world. Notice how limp it is, like a ragdoll. Receptive to my commands. Receptive to your inner and deepest desires. I now hold you from behind. [Whispering] You are exactly where you belong. Here, with me, with your mistress. You are delicate and vulnerable to my touch, my voice, my commands, and it feels just right like you have been waiting for this moment your whole life. And you have. Nine.

You may feel a little precum oozing from your erection. It's okay, my pet. You have no control over that, and I permit it. The immense sexual energy you feel vibrates through every cell in your body. It feels like a gust of wind that washes over you, sprinkling the sensations as it passes you. Feel the tingling that goes from head to toe, growing more intense as it approaches your navel and genital area. You are becoming larger down there. You feel your juices leaking down your skin as you take in the scent of your mistress. Eight. That's good.

Your subconscious mind is now more receptive than ever to the sound of my voice. Your arousal is so intense, and I know that you must be thinking about retreating back to your external reality to touch yourself. But remember that your mistress owns you and that you are now allowed to finish without my permission. Is that understood? Good boy. You're an obedient slave, aren't you?

That feeling overwhelming you right now, as though there's a little bit of pressure that runs down your chest. You feel butterflies in your stomach; all your worries stripped away with nothing on your mind but your identity. You are a submissive man. A pet. My pet. And it feels exhilarating to finally be yourself with your domina here to care for you. Yes, I am always going to be here. Seven.

Breathe in very deeply until there's no room for more air. That's good. Now hold it for just a couple of seconds. And breathe out until there's no more air in your chest. As you breathe in and out, I want you to picture your arousal growing more intense, to the point that it may feel a little painful. But a good kind of pain. The kind of pain you feel when your desire is almost insatiable, when you're voracious for a domina to put you in your place. And I am right here, right behind you, embracing you from behind and guiding you through every step. Six. Breathe in.

One....two...three...four...five. Just a couple of seconds. And out. One...two...three...four...five.

Six. Feel my skin against yours. It's soft and warm, and it makes you feel safe with me. Breathe in and out, and feel me running my fingers through your hair. You are so weak for me. You are so delicate in my presence. You cannot imagine your life without your mistress. Your mistress is all you think about during your waking hours, and the only person you see in your dreams. You obey me without question and enjoy it. Submission fills you with inexplicable feelings of great euphoria. Five.

Your muscles are so limp in my arms. You have completely let go, and you feel weightless. You are floating with me. Feel the gentle breeze caressing your arousal. You feel warm, and you can't help but smile. Your eyes are getting heavier in this dream-like state. This feels like a lucid dream that takes you to an alternate reality.

You feel an incredible sense of ecstasy coursing through your veins, and it's hitting your body like a wave, spreading to every limb. You feel a ticklish tingle rushing down your body. It's very pleasant and relaxing. With every word I say, you are falling deeper into a suggestible trance. Your subconscious mind now automatically recognizes my voice and immediately obeys me. You know that I am your guide and mistress, and you trust the process. Four.

See how wonderful it feels to levitate, to feel the air around you envelop you entirely. You have never felt so good before. You are overwhelmed with feelings of erotic euphoria. This truly feels like a second reality, and it's one that you always come back to. You always come back to your mistress, and you obey her every word without second thoughts. Three. Feel my gentle pecks down your neck, notice how real it feels. You will always remember this incredible trance and the soothing effects it has on your mood. Soon, it will start to feel like your natural state. You will tap back into this state effortlessly and easily.

Two. Your mind and body both feel incredibly relaxed and vulnerable to me. You are fully aroused, and the sensation is traveling through every nerve in your body. You feel the pressure of it, but it's a pleasant kind of pressure. The sensation is warm, and it pulsates through your arousal. Feel the vibrations that run through you. My voice and my touch only intensify the feeling. Your body now knows how to automatically sink deep into this trance the next time you hear my voice.

One. Your arousal is at its maximum. Feel your warm juices leaking. You are throbbing and twitching, eager for the next time we meet again. You are an obedient pet. Submission to your mistress makes you hard. I am always on your thoughts, and you always long for me. When you exit this trance, you will find it hard to wait until you come back to me. Thoughts of me flow through your mind during your waking and sleeping hours. You will remember how wonderful it felt. You will awake refreshed, with the aftereffect of this trance still lingering until you come back to me.

When you awaken, you are permitted to release the tension of your arousal, and it will feel like nothing you have ever experienced before, a highly erotic out-of-body experience. You will think of only me when you finish. You will think of your mistress and the sound of her voice. And now, every time you feel aroused, you will find the need to turn to me and no one else. You know that your mistress owns you and your body.

You are now slowly awakening from the trance, and when I snap my fingers, you will completely exit the trance and open your eyes. You will continue feeling relaxed and stress-free, and you will remember that only your mistress can have such an effect. When you hear the snap of my fingers, you will immediately open your eyes and return to your external reality with a completely different perspective. You will be calm and composed until you return for another journey with your mistress.

Script Three - ASMR for men (makes you super horny)

I want you to find somewhere comfortable to be before we begin. A dark room where you can rest on a bed would be ideal. Make sure to turn off your phone and to avoid any distractions. I would urge you to lay down and rest your head on stacked pillows if needed. This position will help you relax and become more responsive faster. Slowly feel yourself letting go and allow your eyelids to row heavier until they close. Take in a deep breath until you feel pressure on your diaphragm, hold it for a few seconds, then exhale slowly and deeply. Good. You're doing fantastic so far.

At first, you may feel a little resistance against going into a trance. A part of your body may feel itchy, or you may suddenly remember an errand that you have forgotten to do. Simply let those thoughts pass by, and shift your focus back to the present moment. It may help to suck in a deep breath, as loudly as you can, through your nose. And to purposely blow out loud enough for you to hear it consciously. This will allow your mind to focus on the rhythms of your breathing. That's right. You're doing great.

And now, I want you to picture yourself in the nude. You open your eyes in your mind's eye, and you find yourself naked on a beach. Your surroundings look familiar, and there is no one there but yourself. Hear the sound of the waves crashing. Take a lungful of the salty air. Breathe in deeply, hold it for a few seconds, then breathe out very slowly until there's no air in your lungs. Good. You're doing great so far.

Feel the warm sand grazing at your skin. You have been sitting there for a while, enjoying the breeze, and awaiting your domina's orders. I want you to stand up and walk toward the shore. There's no hurry, so there's no need to rush your way there. Take your time to feel your feet sinking into the sand with every step that you take forward. The sand sneaks between your toes, and it washes away the moment you step in the sea. The water is a little chilly, but you get used to it very quickly. Keep going until your body is completely submerged.

Excellent. Now, lay back and enjoy the buoyant feeling of the waves carrying you around. You are no longer doing much effort, and you're simply letting the waves decide where you head next. The water now feels warm on your skin and on your genitals. You lay on your back, and there's no other sound other than my voice guiding you and the birds overhead.

Feel a wave of relaxation washing over you. Feel yourself growing weightless by the second. In the same position, I want you to continue deep breathing and to focus on the sensations in every part of your body. Breathe in deeply. One. Two. Three. Four. Five. Hold it for just a few seconds, and as you exhale, notice how much more relaxed your muscles are. It feels as though you are floating in your external universe. Your shoulders are more relaxed, your spine is more relaxed, and your whole body just feels like a kite, waiting to be directed and guided.

With every word I say, you will sink deeper into a trance. Whenever you hear my voice, you will automatically go into a dream-like state where I speak directly to your subconscious mind, where I speak directly to your inner desires. My voice makes you instantly feel aroused. My voice makes you feel reassured and safe. You trust your mistress and this process, and you will follow through and follow my rules to a T. It feels as though you're falling asleep, but your subconscious mind is wide awake and ready to receive my commands. I now speak to your subconscious mind.

I want you to feel the gentle waves caressing your growing arousal. It's hard for you to contain yourself when you're in the nude, especially in your domina's presence. Yes, that's right. I'm right there with you, and I will guide you through every step. As you continue to enjoy the water underneath you, pushing you up to the surface, I don't want you to get rid of any thoughts that flow through your mind right now. Simply label them, and imagine putting them away in the recesses of your mind until you can come back to them. If you have any worries that keep you from focusing on looking inward and embracing your sensations, do not push them away. Doing so would create resistance, and you would only have a harder time focusing. Simply recognize the emotion or thought and put it away, knowing that you can come back to it when the time is right.

As you breathe in deeply and categorize your thoughts, I want you to feel my physical presence with you. You can feel me slowly approaching you from behind, snaking my arms around you and lifting you up. You don't look my way, but you can feel that I am naked. Your penis enlarges, and you can feel your arousal growing. This almost happens instantly now, as soon as you listen to the sound of my voice.

Breathe in deeply, and let it out. Feel my hands holding you around the waist before I slowly make my way to your arousal. You're so hard. I haven't even touched you yet, and you're already oozing precum. You're quite a naughty sub, aren't you? I like that. You feel so good in my hands. Feel my fingers wrapped around your shaft, sliding up and down under the surface of the water. We are both floating in the gentle waves, our bodies inseparable. You can feel my erect nipples on your back, and you want to turn around, but you're not allowed to. Not yet. When the time is right, we will go back to the shore. For now, I want you to keep breathing deeply.

Every time you exhale, you feel your arousal growing bigger and harder. I want you to send a feeling of tingles to your arousal. Feel how instantaneous that was for my voice to say it, and for your body to feel it as a response. Feel how swiftly your bodily senses react to my commands. I have total control over your body. I have total control over your thoughts and sensations. Whenever I tell you to feel something, you immediately sense it. You feel everything intensely in this reality. Everything feels amplified and arousing. You are addicted to this feeling and to everything your domina allows you to experience. You are in awe with your mistress and how she makes you feel. You are such an obedient pet, aren't you? Now, continue to breathe in and out. Feel the goosebumps running down your skin. Feel that pleasant pressure on your chest, the tingles in your belly, the throbbing of your hard cock. Your mistress is in complete control of your senses, and the thought of it alone makes you feel more aroused.

Breathe in very slowly and deeply. Hold it in for just a few seconds, and feel how much larger your cock is getting with every breath you take. You feel overwhelmed with intense sexual energy – mine and yours. You physically feel my presence as I hold you from behind. You feel safe and reassured. Breathe in deeply. Hold your breath for me, and release very slowly until there's no more air in your chest.

You are doing fantastic. Your body is automatically giving in to my voice, giving in to my commands. You no longer have to think about going into a trance when you listen to me, and your mind immediately knows what to do. You still feel my gentle touch, the tips of my fingers running up and down your inner thighs. You like being teased, don't you, pet? That's right. Feel my fingers lightly flick the ridge of your cock and press ever-so-slightly on your sensitive head. You feel yourself squirming, but you know you're not allowed to make a sound. Not without your mistress's permission.

My touch is making you sink deeper into a hypnotic trance, where you can feel nothing but my touch, where you can hear nothing the sound of my voice blending in with the crashing waves and reassuring you that you're in s safe space. You are in my arms, and you are right where you belong. Your body is weightless, and you feel the tension fading away as your cock gets harder. You're so hard, and you can't stop whimpering. I love the little sounds you make for me and only me. Your body, your thoughts, and your desire are mine to claim, and no one else's. You were born to submit to women. You were born to submit to me. Nothing feels more fulfilling than finally releasing that sexual tension and letting go of all the repression that you have been forced to endure. You feel weightless and free when you are with me. You feel weightless and free during consensual acts of submission.

Yes, you're doing fantastic. I want you to feel yourself effortlessly letting go of any resistance. Notice how differently you feel without any feelings of shame or resistance. Your sexual desires are valid. You are worthy of being dominated. You deserve to fulfill your sexual desires freely and openly. And now shift your focus back to your domina. We are floating together, our skins touching underwater. Your balls are in my hands, while my other hand lightly strokes you. Your breathing is getting heavier. You are getting heavier as you feel overwhelmed with your arousal, but you continue to float above the waves, in my arms. You are getting impatient. Automatically, you now visualize your cock getting harder; you see it throbbing for your mistress with every breath you take. Breathe in deeply and release. Your heart beats are getting faster, and you feel a climax approaching. Remember that we need to take it slow. You are not permitted to touch yourself, and if you obey me, only then will you receive your reward.

Do not be alarmed. I know that you've already made a mess down there, but that was out of your control. I'll allow it, but you're not allowed to finish without my permission. Right now, you are fully aroused. You find it hard to wait for your reward, but you're going to hold it for me. You're going to hold it for your mistress. Feel the arousal pulsating through your erection, it twists and turns for me as I stroke it. My grip is firmer.

You are squirming for more. This is starting to feel like an out-of-body experience. You are overcome by erotic euphoria as you twist and turn for my touch. [Chuckles] I can feel your juices oozing out. Whenever I ask you a yes or no question, I want you to answer with, "Yes, domina" in your mind or in a whisper. Every time I say the word domina, you are going to feel me stroke you, firmer and faster. Your domina wants you to cum for her, but not yet. We will get there when you obey. Does this feel good, my pet? Good. You have been so good, and you deserve to cum.

Keep your eyes closed and continue breathing deeply. You don't need to hold your breath. Just breathe in slowly and deeply, and let it out. Feel your erection throb to my touch; feel it throb with every breath you take. You feel the arousal coursing through your veins. Your domina is the only person you think about. Only your domina can give you permission to cum. You submit to your domina without question. You know that your domina owns you, and the thought of it turns you on like nothing else. Deep down in your subconscious, you desire no one else but your domina. You crave my presence, and you long for me when I'm not there.

Do I make myself clear? Good. Now, I want you to feel me letting go of you and sinking underwater. Your erection is slowly sliding into my mouth, and you have never felt your erection this sensitive before. Your domina's tongue flicks and plays along your ridge. I permit you to moan and whimper. You may moan only for your domina. Do I make myself clear? Excellent. You're such a good boy. Every time you hear me say the word domina, you will feel me suck you harder and deeper. You are so close to the edge, but I am not done with you, pet. Your domina will take this a little slow.

Feel how warm my mouth is. Feel the difference in warmth as I pull you out and inside my mouth. I want you to throw your head back and indulge in the feeling.

The warmth of my tongue against your erection. You only feel this immense pleasure from your domina. You crave this pleasure every waking minute of your day. Your domina fuels you with immense sexual energy and sex appeal. This feels like a dream-like state, a wet dream that you will awaken from feeling refreshed and reinvigorated. Your release will be the most satisfying feeling you will have ever experienced. I want you to moan for your domina. I want to hear you. Do I make myself clear? Yes, that's the noise I'm looking for.

It's time for us to go back to shore. While you float in the water, I want you to close your mind's eye for a few seconds. As soon as you open it, you find yourself on shore with your domina. You are kneeling before me, and I guide you to get on all fours. Feel the sand grating against your knees and hands. I stand right behind you, and you are ready to receive whatever I give you. Isn't that so, my obedient pet? Good. I enjoy keeping you. You're so much fun to use and abuse [chuckles]. And I like the view from where I'm standing.

I'd like you to spread your legs a little more. No, a little more than that. Yes, that's right. I like positions that are most vulnerable. I can do whatever I want with you, and you will enjoy every. Single. Second. Of. It.

Continue to breathe in and out for me. Every time I say the word domina, you will feel pressure around your cock and feel yourself throbbing. Feel me stroking your balls and cock with my delicate fingers. My grasp is getting firmer, but I don't want to hear so much as a whimper from you. Your cock is throbbing in my hand as I jerk you off and caress your balls. I can see you're already squirming, but you're not allowed to cum yet. Feel my grasp getting firmer. My hand is lightly squeezing at the ridge, flicking you ever-so-slightly to watch you twist and turn for me. I love the way your ass moves for me, wanting more.

Feel me sliding a finger inside your ass. My finger circles deep inside you, and you start to moan. Didn't your domina forbid you from making noises? [Slapping] Or are you a brat that likes to be spanked while getting his ass fingered? [Slapping] Do you like it when your domina turns your ass red? [Slapping and chuckling] I think you do. Do you feel the heat? Do you feel the sting on your ass? [Slapping] You're such a brat, but I'll still give you what you've been waiting for. After I've had my fun with you.

I know two fingers in your tight ass feel a little much, but you're doing good. Is it too much when I massage your prostate while jerking you off? Your body is having a visceral reaction, and you're getting louder. [Slapping] Your domina is very proud of how much you can handle. [Continued slapping] You're taking it all at once, and you're doing brilliantly. Your domina permits you to cum. I know you're close, I can feel it in the way your back is arching. Your ass is completely loosened up for me now. [Moans] I see your cock is already leaking. Cum for me, pet. I know you love this part, when I jerk you off so quickly your eyes roll back. I know you love it when your domina abuses you. You're such an obedient pet. Cum for your domina. Cum for me. Yes, you're so close to the edge.

[Pause] Look at all that mess. I want you to get back on your knees and turn around to look at the mess you've made. Now, my hands are covered in your juices, and you need to clean it up. Yes, just like that. No need to do it quickly. Take as much time as you need. I know this was intense for you, so I'm going to give you a few minutes to take a breather before you awaken from this reality.

I want you to close your mind's eye and picture yourself back in your room. Do not open your eyes before I command you to. When you awaken from this dream-like state, you're going to feel incredibly refreshed and reinvigorated. You're going to feel euphoric for the rest of the day, and the feeling will continue until you find your way back to me. Your thoughts will revolve around only your domina, and you will refuse to touch yourself without my permission.

When I snap my fingers, you will awaken from this state, and you will experience feelings of joy and extreme composure until we meet again. You will feel like a completely different man. Remember that this state will wear off completely if you're not consistent with our meetings. Until we meet again, my pet.

Script Four - The ultimate pleasure (dirty language)

I want you to find your usual spot for unwinding. Ideally, a dark room where you can lie down on a bed and where there are no distractions that would hinder our progress. You can use a blanket if it makes you feel comfortable, just make sure that you stack pillows to rest your head in an upright position. I need you to stay awake but ultimately relaxed. Are we clear? Good.

Close your eyes, and keep your arms on either of your sides. For his exercise, it's best to have as little to no clothes as possible. Let's start with simple breathing exercises. I want you to breathe in as deeply as you can, hold it in for a few seconds, then slowly release. Breathe in. One. Two. Three. Four. Five. Hold it for a few. And now let go. One. Two. Three. Four. Five. Excellent. Now, repeat this until I tell you to stop.

As you continue to focus on your breathing patterns, I want you to get rid of any thoughts or worries that may be distracting you right now. You can simply tuck the worries away in the recesses of your mind where you can come back for them later whenever you're ready. Right now, let's focus on you and your body. As you breathe in and out deeply, feel a tingling sensation in the crown of your head. The sensation starts out small and barely noticeable, but it continues to grow. It feels like a warm spark on top of your head, and it slowly and pleasantly permeates the rest of your senses. Slowly suck in a deep and long breath. Hold it in for me. And now exhale, feeling yourself becoming one with your senses.

You are now connecting with your body and your sensations. You have finally stopped thinking about your external world and have begun looking inwards. Good. Now, feel this tingling sensation run down your spine and spreading to your every limb. It's gentle, like a delicate numbing sensation that caresses your every nerve. Feel yourself getting warmer and more comfortable. Your muscles are relaxing now, and it's making you feel lighter, more responsive to your domina's voice. You are letting go completely, and you are ready to receive. You follow your domina's orders without question. Do you feel pressure in your knees? Do you feel the warmth emanating from your body?

Your body is reacting to my words instantaneously. You feel everything your domina tells you to feel. Your mind and body obey me without question. Notice how relaxed your body is right now; you can barely even feel it. You are in a dream-like state where I speak directly to your subconscious mind. Your subconscious mind immediately recognizes my voice and obeys. Whenever I say the word domina, you are going to feel yourself getting more and more aroused. Every command I throw your way will make you harder. The soothing sound of my voice makes you automatically enter slave mode. Am I understood? Good. I want you always to respond to me in your mind or in a whisper and address me as your domina.

The pattern of your breathing has slowed down. It's time for you to meet your domina for your ultimate pain and pleasure. Today, you're going to be the little sex toy that I do whatever I please with. Breathe in slowly, and out. You feel your eyes getting heavier and heavier with every word I speak. You feel yourself gently being pulled by a wave, a deep dream-like trance. Feel yourself gently falling, floating downward until you reach the bottom, where your reality is weaved with the sound of my voice. Yes, that's right. Let's breathe in one more time, as deeply as you can, and hold it for just a couple of seconds. As you exhale, I want you to imagine the air coming out of your mouth, weaving new scenery.

You find yourself in your mistress's bedroom, but you can't move because you're chained to the bed. You can only see the ceiling, and you can hear your domina moving around the bedroom. Take a deep breath, and let it out without holding it in. Feel the blood coursing through your veins, and the tingling in your belly. You know why you're here, and I know you're impatient. But I will take my time with you, and I want you to obey my every command. Or else, you may be subject to punishment. Do I make myself clear, slaveboy?

Good. Let's play a little game where you already have a head-start. I am going to count down from ten to one. As I descend, you're going to feel your cock getting harder. When I reach number one, you will be fully erected. Is my little pet ready to impress his domina?

Good boy. Ten. You feel me walking toward you. [Squeaking] I'm climbing the bed, getting on top of you. You finally see my face, and it's exactly how you have pictured it, perhaps a little sexier. Nine. Feel your cock throbbing and twitching in excitement. You're dying to be punished and rewarded. Eight. Your face is getting warmer, and you feel sweat beads running down your forehead. You're both nervous and excited. And you're definitely aroused and a little frustrated. Seven. Feel the pressure rising in your erection. Your cock is getting harder, anticipating my touch.

Breathe in deeply and let exhale without holding your breath. Your body is reacting exactly as I command it to. Your domina has full control over your thoughts and sensations. You feel everything I say, and you feel it intensely. You feel the blood rushing through your arousal, and your body is lightly shaking, begging me to grace it with my touch. Six. And now, feel me running my finger down your chest and to your torso and navel. Goosebumps are quickly forming on your skin, and your thin body hair is rising. Five. You are breathing deeply, and as you release, you let go of any resistance. You are completely vulnerable to your mistress. You are entirely responsive to my voice. I am in alignment with everything you desire in a mistress. Five.

My fingers stop at your hard cock, and I begin stroking you. My touch is gentle but firm. Feel my delicate fingers caressing you, rubbing you, jerking you off as your breathing begins to get heavier. I have only just begun playing with my toy, and it's already oozing precum. Are you getting a little too impatient, pet? You better have better control over yourself next time. Four. Feel the intense sensation in your cock pulsating through your limbs, and every part of your body, feel it echoing in your every vein. It's elevating and transcendent, and you know that this is just the tip of the iceberg of our journey, and much more visceral reactions await you. Three.

You are entirely lubricated now, and it's making matters easier for me. My hands easily slide up and down your cock, and the sensations follow the motion. I feel your throbbing in my hands. Two. I feel you twitching as your body begs for more. Feel the pressure tighten around your cock as you reach a full erection for your domina. Feel your cock getting larger and flipping to an upright position. One. You are now fully erect.

Your skin feels so sensitive, much more sensitive to my touch than it is to anyone else's in your external world. You are tantalized. You are fully aroused and readier than ever for my touch. Feel a pleasant pinch in your nipples, where I touch you with my other hand. The pinch gets firmer and warmer. I love the way your cock feels in my hand, slave. [Chuckles] I have a pleasant surprise for you. We're going to play another game, and this one is far more exciting. When I unchain you, I want you to flip around on your other side and get on all fours. [Shackling] Yes, just like that. Good. [Shackling] Now, let's stay in this position for a while, where you can't see me nor anticipate what I'm about to do. Your domina loves the view from here. You look so weak and vulnerable to me. You can't keep your body still. You are aching for your domina's touch.

[Slapping] No matter how hard I spank your ass, I don't want to hear a single sound from you. Are we clear? Good. I want you always to address me as your domina. [Slapping] Feel the numbing sensation growing on your reddening ass cheeks. [Slapping] Your domina loves to give both your cheeks equal attention. We better make them match in color. [Slapping] I love the way your cock twitches for you domina whenever she lays her hand on you. Your body is mine. [Slapping] Your mind is mine. [Slapping]

Feel a wave of euphoria wash over you as you receive your domina's punishment. You feel the pain and pleasure in your entire body, enveloping you like cold smoke. Feel yourself merging with your sensations, becoming one. You only feel this kind of erotic euphoria in the presence of your mistress. You are entranced by your domina. You are obsessed with sex and submission. You follow your desires without shame. Your sexual needs make you stronger the more you fulfill them, and you feel it now, coursing through your veins like a wave of sparkling energy. Shift your focus to where you feel me touching you. [Slapping] Right there. You feel the warmth of my hand and the warmth of your skin merging. You are getting number, and you feel it traveling down your legs. Your hard cock is throbbing for more. [Slapping] You're such an obedient slave, aren't you? That's right.

Your domina is so proud of how much pain you can hold up. Feel my touch rewarding you, caressing you where it's warm and painful. My touch makes you feel tingles in your skin. It's okay to gasp. I love the noises my little slaveboy makes. But you must remember not to touch yourself without your domina's permission, no matter how intense the craving gets. Your domina owns you. I am everything you desire and everything you know you must obey. You obey my commands naturally and spontaneously, as though I am the voice of your own thought. I am the voice of your own thoughts. You are in awe with the erotic experiences your domina provides you. You are addicted to the sound of my voice, and it makes you hard the moment you hear it.

And now, we move on to please your mistress. If you want permission to cum, you must first earn it by pleasuring your domina. I stand right before you now, on my knees, with my pussy lips spread for your tongue while you're still on all fours. Stick it out and feel the air around it. You feel the sensation deeply in this second reality. [Cracks whip] I'm going to continue whipping your pathetic ass as you tongue fuck me. Flick my clit with your tongue, suck on it, your life depends on it. Yes, make your domina proud. [Moaning] That's right, that's the spot right there. [Cracks whip] Feel the strands of my whip sting your delicate skin. Feel your ass getting warmer with every lashing. [Cracks whip] Don't you fucking stop. Right there, and keep going. Feel the warmth of my cunt with your tongue. Feel the softness of my skin. It's making you more aroused, more frustrated. You know your reward will be promising. [Cracks whip] Your cock is throbbing with every lashing and every flick of your tongue. Don't stop, slaveboy. Don't you dare stop tongue fucking your domina until I say so. [Continued moaning] You're a natural. You were born to submit to me. [Louder moaning] I'm so close, keep going. Keep going, don't you fucking stop. Keep going, my pet. [Loud moaning] Oh, fuck. You're such a good boy. Now, clean up the mess you made. Yes, just like that. Good boy.

You have been doing good so far, and it's safe to say that you have finally earned your reward. Has your cock been leaking as you tongue fucked your domina? I think it has. [Wet smacking] All those juices will prove handy. Feel my finger circling your asshole. It's twitching for me, ready for me to fuck you. Feel the warmth of my other hand jerking you off. My grip is firm, and I know just where to caress you. Your balls feel so warm when I cup them in my hand like this. You love this spot, don't you? [Slapping] You love it when I bust your balls like this. [Slapping] So sensitive and warm. [Slapping] Your cock is throbbing for me. It's wriggling, begging me not to keep my hands away. [Chuckling] You are such a needy slaveboy. You've made me cum, and now it's time to make you cum for your domina.

I'm going to do another countdown, from ten to one. When I say one, you are granted permission to cum, and you may not cum a second before that. Do I make myself clear, pet? Good. I love how obedient you are to your domina. Ten. Feel the tip of my finger sliding inside you. You have such a tight asshole; it's a little too tight. We may need a plug for this. [Chuckles] Yes, this is much better. Don't turn around; I don't want you to look at it. I want you to feel it sink into your ass. Feel the tip slowly being squeezed in. You're uncomfortable at first. Nine. It's all the way in, and this feels better than you have anticipated. Feel the pressure inside your ass. [Slapping] Feel it intensify when my hand lands on your ass. That's right; I want you to squirm for me. Just like that.

[Chains unshackling] I've unchained you. Eight. You can lay down on your back now. You'll feel the pressure of the plug squeezing deeper inside you. Your nipples are hard, and so are you. Is your cock ready for my reward? Are you ready to fuck your domina's cunt and cum? Seven. Feel my warm thighs touching yours as I climb on top of you. You love looking at those tits, don't you? No, you're not permitted to touch them today. Keep your hands to your sides. Six.

My warm breath beats on your face now as I lean toward you. Now, look me straight into my eye as I slide my cunt down your cock. Five. You are sliding inside my tight pussy slowly, and you feel a rush through your veins, echoing the throbbing in your hard cock. Feel my wet walls envelop your cock. You are deep inside your mistress, and it's nothing like you've ever felt before. Four. As I rock back and forth, I want you to focus on all the sensations you feel coursing through your body. Your throbbing cock inside your domina, the goosebumps on your skin, raising all your body hair. You feel it in your chest, and your heart beats faster.

[Moaning] You feel so good inside me. I'm going faster and deeper now. [Louder moaning] Feel yourself getting closer and closer to the edge. You feel the climax approaching like you're going to explode. You feel your cock getting more sensitive. Your whole body is warmer, radiating all the sexual energy you feel trapped within you. [Continued moaning] You're so close, and your domina permits you to cum. Cum for me, my pet. Feel your cock thrusting into your domina, the warmth inside her, the pleasant wet noises making you closer. You're so close. I want you to cum for me. I want you to cum all over your domina. [Continued moaning] Yes, that's right. You're so close, slave, don't you disappoint me. Cum for your domina. You're so close. Cum for your mistress. [Louder moaning] You're so close, and I want your juices in my mouth. Cum for your domina and let her taste her sweet slave. Yes, cum for me. Feel my lips around your cock; feel it deep inside my throat. It's firm and swift, and my lips flick your ridge with every stroke. You're so close. Now, cum for your domina.

[Muffled moaning] You taste just how your domina likes it. Mmm, you have been so good, and you've finally received your reward. When you exit this dream-like state, you're going to continue thinking about this and about your domina. You are addicted to your one and only mistress, and you will always find a way back to her for more. When you get some rest, you are going to continue meeting me in your dreams and letting me fuck you there, too. You know that I own you wherever you go, and you always cannot wait to see me again.

I want you to remember that you're not permitted to cum without my permission. I permeate your thoughts and desires. You will continue to long for the sound of my voice throughout your day. You will be able to focus and be productive while I stay in the back of your mind at all times. You submit to your domina and only her. Now, breathe in deeply, and let it out. And again. I want you to breathe in. One. Two. Three. Four. Five. Hold it for a few seconds, and as you deeply exhale, I want you to think about going back to where you first started. You are back to your dark and quiet room in your external reality, but your mind is still here. When I snap my fingers, you are going to awaken and open your eyes immediately. You will remember all my affirmations and commands, and you will continue to follow them throughout your day wherever you go. I will wait for you, pet. Until next time. [Snapping]

Script Five - Classic femdom hypno session (will you get permission to cum?)

Hello there. I knew you'd find your way to me. You're insatiable, aren't you? Well, that's what I'm here for. But before we get there, we will have to work on getting you to a state of mindfulness that allows you to submit to me completely. Do you understand? Good. You're an obedient little sub, aren't you? Now, I want you to be patient with me and follow every step I walk you through to the T. I want you to sit somewhere comfortable where there are no distractions, and completely lose yourself to my voice. That's right. I'm here for you. If you do exactly as I say and avoid any and all distractions, I promise you that you will have the most erotic experience yet. I'm waiting.

Are you ready now? All cozied up? Good sub. Now, I want to make it clear that my voice will put you in a deep trance as you completely lose yourself to my every command, so make sure you're not driving or operating machinery. I want you to be safe. And feel free to picture me right there next to you. I look exactly like the dominatrix you've always dreamed of. Try to be at a space where it's dark, too. I don't want you to open your eyes until I say so. Lastly, I want you to turn off your phone, if possible. We can't have any distractions, or else I'll be very cross with you, my pet. And you don't ever want me to be cross with you.

Now that we have everything covered let me introduce myself. I am your mistress. The one and only mistress you'll ever need. If you let yourself go completely, you will find yourself completely drawn to my voice and my commands, but you will awaken when relieved, and you will feel empowered. As your mistress, I will care for your every need, but you must never disobey, and if you do, there is always a price to pay for it. But it will never come to that, will it, my obedient slut? Good. I'm glad we understand each other.

I'm going to count down to five. When I get to five, I want you to close your eyes and stop your thoughts from wandering. Whenever your train of thought seems to sway, don't be hard on yourself –that's my job– and simply just guide your thoughts back to my voice. To me. Yes, that's right. I'm not going anywhere until I'm done with you. You'll notice that my rhythm will be slower now. Just ride the wave and let your eyes weigh down until you fall into a deep trance, the only thoughts you are forming are those that I command you to.

Impressive. You're doing great, my good pet. I may think about keeping you [softly chuckles]. Now that your focus is completely on me, you may feel your body trying to distract you. You may feel the need to itch here and there, but if you focus on my voice, the feeling will go away. This is natural and only happens because your body is too excited for what is to come.

Now, let's get to counting. Are you ready? Good boy. One. Two. Three. Four. Five. Good. There are no visuals to distract us now, and we can finally work on some light breathing exercises. I want you to inhale and hold your breath for five seconds before I command you to exhale for another five seconds. This will help you loosen up to me, and we don't want to be tense, do we? We'll save that for when I'm through with you. We'll repeat this three times.

On the count of three, I want you to take a deep breath and then hold it. One. Two. Three. Hold your breath and count to five. Good. Now breathe out until you feel your diaphragm tighten. And again. One. Two. Three. Hold it. Now breathe out. We'll do this one more time. One. Two. Three. Hold your breath. And now you can breathe out. What we've done now are breathing exercises that will help put you in theta mode much more efficiently. This is when you'll be completely relaxed and suggestible to my commands, allowing you to submit to me completely. Every sensation will feel as though I am there with you. [Softly] And I am.

We have completed the first step. We'll now proceed to the next step. During this breathing exercise, I want you to be seated in a dark room. Pitch black, if possible. And I want you to sit comfortably on a bed or a sofa. Keep your legs crossed, as though you're about to meditate. If the position is uncomfortable, I permit you to lie down. Brilliant. You're doing great so far; you're such a good boy. With your eyes still closed, suck in deep breaths through your nose, and let out long exhales through your mouth. I don't want you to focus on anything but the sound of my voice and the rhythm of your breathing. Don't let your mind drift off, or you may fall asleep. I want you wide awake but stay with me. Now, let's start. Deep breaths. Slow exhales. We won't count the number of times you have to do this. With every breath you take in, I want you to picture drawing any distracting thoughts, and exhaling them out as gray smoke. In with your thoughts, and out. We can get back to them later, but right now, there's nothing on your mind but the sound of my voice, following my every command effortlessly, and submitting yourself to me completely. Draw in, exhale. I am your mistress, and you trust my words. You trust the process.

I no longer speak to your conscious mind. Now, I'm directly communicating with your subconscious, where all the deepest desires in the recesses of your mind float to the surface to roam free and unjudged. Or catered to by your mistress. You submit to me willingly and await your prize or punishment. Right now, you may feel your eyes twitching, your conscious mind still struggling to let go. But this will change soon if you follow my every command like the good sub you are.

Now, I need you to picture me how you first imagined me. Don't open your eyes, but know that I'm right there next to you, guiding you with my voice, and looking down at you lovingly with a bright smile on my face. Yes, just like that. But don't get too excited because we're not done with our breathing exercises. We're going to keep counting down your breaths until you fall into a deep trance. You're relaxed now. That's good. I want you more relaxed, in a state of complete submission to me. I will continue telling you what to do, and if you follow your mistress's orders to a T, you will start doing as I say without second thoughts, as though your own mind is speaking to you.

You are fully relaxed now. I need you to be still for me. Don't scratch that eyelid that has been bothering you or move to a more comfortable position. I want your body completely still until I tell you to do otherwise. This time, when you draw in a deep breath, I want you to look at yourself in your spot from a third-person perspective and to see me sitting right there beside you.

Guiding you. You're doing incredible. Do you see how peaceful you look? Now, take a deep breath and don't stop until your chest is full. One. Two. Three. Four. Five. Breathe out, and don't stop until your diaphragm stops you. One. Two. Three. Four. Five. Excellent. You're really good at this. I am now caressing your face, and you see me doing so from where you're standing. Imagine how my soft skin feels on yours as it gently runs down your cheek. My touch is gentle and slow. It is passionate. You are feeling your heart sink and your heart beating faster. You feel a tingle in the groin, and I permit you to feel that way. Just don't touch yourself. Not yet. Not until your mistress says you can.

Now, imagine my fingers running down your neck and caressing your chest. Yes. Just like that. Picture the sensation until you feel a tingling on your skin. You may feel another part of your body right now to be a little itchy. Do not be alarmed, my pet. This is natural, and you should pay no mind to it. Feel my gentle touch running down your torso and stopping at your naval. You are getting goosebumps, and the hairs on your body are now raised. Good. You are beginning to lose yourself to me completely, but we're not quite there yet.

I now want you to focus on your breaths once more. You are back inside your body and no longer watching yourself from afar. I am still beside you, but you cannot see me because your eyes are still closed. Do not open them. We will keep them shut until I permit you to do otherwise. We are now going to work on being in your utmost relaxed yet mindful state. This time, I want you to imagine being physically lighter with every breath that you exhale. Take in a deep breath as long as I count down the seconds. One. Two. Three. Four. Five. Breathe out, and through your mouth. Picture your body getting lighter and lighter. You no longer feel your body pressing against your seat or bed. It slowly feels as though you are floating on air. Breathe in. One. Two. Three. Four. Five. And out. One. Two. Three. Four. Five. One more time, we're going to take in a deep breath. One. Two. Three. Four. Five. And exhale, noticing how much lighter your body feels.

As you listen to my voice, it may feel like you're falling asleep. I don't want you to fight it off because I need your mind focused on only my voice. I promise I will keep you awake and alert because I know you're eager to receive your award if you follow my every step now.

We're almost there, so bear with me. We're going to work on a different exercise that allows you to be mindful of every part of your body. Focus on your eyelids, which have been relaxed for a while now. I want you to follow the motion of your eyes underneath your closed lids. They have been still for a while, but now you may feel your lids twitching, as though your eyelids are squeezed shut.

I need you to focus on the sensation. Feel your eyelids getting warmer and warmer the more you focus on them. Good. Did you feel that? You're getting better at this. And now, we'll move to your lips. Slide your focus down to your lips. It's okay if you feel them shaking slightly. It's only because your mind has shifted its attention to them. They may feel a little dry, but I don't want you to move them too much or wet your lips. Feel the warmth emanating from your skin. Feel the warmth emanating until you feel the heat in your entire face. Your cheeks may tingle, and you may suddenly feel the urge to lower the temperature in your home. But I command you to stay still. We have gone this far, and you're so far doing fantastic.

And now, we finally shift your attention to your groin. It's okay if you feel your member enlarging, and it's okay if you suddenly feel aroused. I permit it. You have been a good sub so far, and if you keep up with me for the next couple of minutes, you will finally receive the award that I know you've been waiting for, and it will be far more intense than how you've initially pictured it. Focus on your genital area and how it tingles when you think about it. Focus your energy there, and feel the warmth emanating, spreading to your every nerve. You may picture me beside you, caressing you ever-so-slightly and sensually. You have been good, and I permit it. Feel the area spreading energy to your entire body, filling you up. Excellent. You're getting very good at this.

Your body feels like it's floating, and your groin is getting warmer by the second. Your whole body now feels the heat. As it envelops you, you feel its intensity overwhelming you with awe. This is the power of your mind. This is what happens when you completely let go and submit yourself to me. As you breathe in and breathe out, pay attention to the rhythm of your breaths and imagine your penis enlarging as you listen to the sound of my voice, knowing an award awaits you soon. Very soon.

Now that you have mastered the sensations in your body, it's time to take it to the next level. I want you to do as I say as if my voice comes from the deep recesses of your mind. As if my voice is your very own, communicating with you inside your head. This time, I'm going to do the exercises with you. I will not count down this time, and you will simply follow my lead. [Inhales and exhales]. Good. Now we're going to repeat that a few times, until you feel yourself falling deeper into a trance, into ultimate relaxation and submission. [Inhales and exhales x4].

[Softly and slower] Excellent. Now, you're ready for your award. As your mistress, I need you to follow my every instruction without question. You are willing to do everything I tell you to do, and you know that it will make you feel a kind of euphoria that you have never experienced before. The kind that only I can give to you whenever I please, and whenever you find your way back to me. Your mistress is here for you. I am right beside you, but I need you to keep your eyes closed for me. Feel my warmth approaching you. Feel my breath beating down your neck as I lean down and brush a finger against your face. My touch – you have felt it before, but now it is far more intense. It's as though I'm right there with you. And I am.

I'm going to guide you through the process now, but every time I command you to do something, I want to hear you respond. In your head. Whenever I order you to do as I please, I want you to answer with "yes, mistress, or "yes, goddess." If you address me as otherwise, this whole process would have been in vain. I will remind you as we go along, but only at first. Every time you say these words, you will feel your cock enlarging and throbbing.

And to do this, I want you to let go of any resistance you hold inside you completely. Your mistress would never do anything to harm you, and everything I command your subconscious is completely in your favor. I promise. Your mistress will tell you exactly what to do, and she is watching you. I am watching you, my obedient sub. Every time you obey my command, you will feel arousal pulsating throughout your entire body.

You will be overwhelmed with sensual euphoria, and you will find your way back to me for more. You are entranced. You are free of resistance. You can feel my presence, as though I am there with you, and you feel my touch to the bone. You are now getting goosebumps. Feel them run down your skin, making a shiver race down your spine. The hairs on your skin are now standing on end. Your body reacts exactly as I command it. You do exactly as I command you.

And now, I need you to start addressing me with the names we have agreed upon before. I need to ask you a few questions before we proceed. Are you ready for your mistress? [Softly] Good. Will you follow my instructions to the letter without giving them second thoughts? Good. I will now begin touching you, but you must never touch yourself. Never without your mistress's permission.

As I now completely take control, you feel my fingertips lightly caressing your bulge. You feel it growing harder, bigger, aching for more. But my touch remains gentle. You feel a throb lightly pulsating throughout your cock, your groin getting warmer and warmer. You are no longer mentally keeping track of the rhythms of your breaths. You are completely focused and in sync with the motion of my hand. My fingers run up and down the fabric of your bottoms. You want my touch to be firmer. But it softly grabs your cock, and you feel it throbbing.

Your cock is rock-hard for your mistress. Do you like this, my obedient sub? Good. You are not permitted to touch yourself. You are doing well. Good boy. I can still feel the resistance you have for this, but it's getting harder to resist your mistress. Every time you hear your mistress's sub call you a good boy, you feel a wave of euphoria and extreme arousal wash over you, taking over your mind and body completely, under the mercy of your mistress. Do you understand me? Good boy. Feel your cock throb for me as you picture me leaning over to you and pulling down your pants. With your mind's eye, watch me slide your cock between my lips. You see me spit on your hard and throbbing cock before I push it back inside my mouth. Do you like that, obedient sub? Good boy.

I permit you to see me naked. I permit you to see me climbing on top of you. My warm and dripping wet cunt engulfs your cock, and now you feel pre-cum oozing. I'll allow it, but you are not permitted to touch yourself. Not yet. You are losing yourself to me completely, powerless against my words. Your heart is racing. Your body is on the verge of shaking as your patience runs low. You want to be inside me more than anything. I can feel it in the way your body fails to lay still. Your breathing is growing heavier.

Wow, you're getting really big! And you haven't even begun touching yourself yet. Good boy. You feel a wave of frustration washing over you, and it heightens as you think of me. You are thinking of how the gentle touch of my fingertips feels on the ridge of your hard cock. You're such a good sub. Pre-cum continues to ooze out of your hard cock. You are watching me as I dabble with your balls, digging my fingers ever-so-slightly into your sensitive skin. Goosebumps are racing down your skin. Your chest is heaving, and you're breaths are growing louder. Good sub. Your body is reacting exactly how I guide it. Good sub. You are my slave, and you always do exactly as I say. Good sub. Your resistance to my commands have completely lifted, and you are completely powerless to me. The image of my lips wrapped around your hard cock, pushing it deep down my throat, flicking the head with my tongue, is making you hard as a rock. You cannot wait to be permitted to release all this tension. And you won't until I say you can. Good sub.

You love obeying me, don't you, my obedient pet? Good sub. You are feeling overwhelmed with arousal. Your body is completely in my control, doing exactly as I say. Beg me to grant you permission to cum. Beg your mistress. Every time you say "please, mistress," your cock will enlarge even further and throb more vigorously for me. You are dying to relieve yourself, and I now permit you to touch yourself. Keep your eyes closed. You will find yourself already moist, and that's okay. Don't reach out for any lube. Stay where you are, and touch yourself to the sound of my voice. My voice fills you to the brim with ecstasy. This is the hardest you have ever felt your cock. Good sub. You earned your reward.

You are permitted to fuck your mistress. What do you say? That's right. Good sub. I want you to go faster. You are inside me. You are inside your mistress, thrusting in and out of me as hard and as fast as you can. My pussy is warm and tight, and it's nothing like you've ever felt before. You are incredibly close to climaxing. Your heart is beating faster, and it feels as though you are out of breath. My massive tits are now bouncing in sync with your thrusts, and my moans are a siren's song to your ears. I permit you to cum, my pet. You may cum. Cum for your mistress. Cum all over me. I command you to. You feel yourself even closer. You are cumming to my voice. You are cumming to the image of my massive bouncing tits as I jump up and down your hard and throbbing cock.

Cum, slave. Oh my. Your juices are so warm inside me. I throw my head back in ecstasy, climaxing in unison with you. You are incredible. You are such a good sub, and you must find your way back to me. I command you to. I now permit you to open your eyes. You may feel a little dazed and slightly dissociated. Do not be alarmed, my pet. This is just the effect of my charm. You will continue to be drawn to me every day. When you come back to visit your mistress, she will be here, ready to make you cum again. Until next time, my good sub.

Script Six - The vulgar rough trance session for men

Hello, slave. I knew you would find your way to me swiftly. You have found your mistress, and I would guess that you're ready for your humiliation. But I prefer to take things slow. Allow me to introduce myself. I go by Mistress, and you may not call me otherwise unless I specifically ask you to. If your tongue happens to slip, or if you do anything else that goes against my rules, you shall receive a special kind of punishment. Isn't that why you're here, after all?

I will now briefly wait for you to retreat to a quiet and dark room, where you have uninterrupted privacy and where you can comfortably obey my commands without question. **[Five-second pause]** A bed is a great choice. You may lay down and close your eyes. Yes, your Mistress permits it. A dark spot will help you feel more relaxed. I can feel how tense you are, and I notice how your mind wanders to question whether or not such audio would work on you. Especially for such a skeptical mind like yours. But I promise you that you'll feel the drastic difference at the end of our hypnosis session. Remember that every time you come back to me, the session will feel more intense. If you listen to me often enough, you will be able to garner the incredibly erotic sensations that you will feel soon on your own.

As my slave and my pet, I expect you to do as I say without second thoughts. You are not permitted to use your free will. And this includes cumming without permission. I may seem quite stern, but I can be lenient when you please your mistress. You have come here for a reason, and it's because you wish to be hypnotized by your mistress's charm. By her divine scent and her soft skin that you feel brush against yours. In this case, I am here for you, but I will have to ask you to do one thing on your own: to become completely powerless against my voice, my commands, and my will. You will let yourself go completely, under the mercy of your mistress.

I want you to close your eyes slowly and begin focusing on you're the rhythm of your breath. Every time I command you to do something, the way I just did, I expect you to respond to me. You can answer me in your mind or out loud. Whatever feels comfortable for you. But I need you to say my name whenever you obey your Mistress. Good. And now that we're clear, I want you to shift your focus back on your breaths. Right now, they're very shallow. I want you to take in one deep breath, so long as I count to four. One. Two. Three. Four. Good, now breathe out. One. Two. Three. Four. How does that feel? It's only a little laborious now.

Feel my voice rush through your veins. Feel yourself already losing yourself to me as you listen to my words. I want you to relax in that position completely. Keep your hands on your chest, or rest your arms alongside you. But I don't want you to move unless your Mistress asks you to do otherwise. Understood, slave? Good boy. You're doing excellent so far. Because your mind is so focused right now, on my voice and on the air you're sucking into your lungs, you may feel a sudden urge to itch somewhere on your body, and this place may change with time. Do not be alarmed. This is a natural reaction, but I need you to pay no heed to it. You must remain in your position until I ask you to change it.

Keep your eyes closed. At this phase, I will need you to work with your Mistress before you can reap your reward and be punished like the little slut that you are. We are going to start by working on your mindfulness. In this stage, we will start by focusing on your breath and then slowly extend our way to the rest of your body. Do you understand me, my pet? Good. Inhale one deep breath. One. Two. Three. Four. And exhale. One. Two. Three. Four. As you take in a breath, I want you to picture yourself, alleviating your mind of any and all thoughts that may disturb your concentration. As you suck in a breath, draw in a worry that's on your mind. This can be a daily worry, or it can simply be the stress of trying not to think. Because your mistress knows that you're a beginner, she permits you to have wandering thoughts at this stage of our exercise.

Now, take another deep breath, drawing in any thought on your mind. One. Two. Three. Four. As you exhale, you alleviate yourself of all restraints that may hinder our progress in this session. Good. You're doing great. And again. Breathe in. One. Two. Three. Four. And out. One. Two. Three. Four. You now feel lighter, and feel yourself gradually submitting more to your Mistress. You trust your Mistress, and you know that your reward will be an incredibly erotic experience – almost ethereal. Let's do this one more time. Breathe in. One. Two. Three. Four. And exhale. Do you feel how much lighter your body is now? You are now letting go completely.

We're going to repeat the previous exercise, but we're going to focus on something different. This time, I want you to imagine letting me in and keeping all wandering thoughts out. Feel my voice permeate your senses as I completely take over your subconscious mind. I control your thoughts. I control your emotions. I control your sensations. Every time you hear the sound of my voice, you feel your cock enlarge, and your arousal amplify. You are powerless against the power of my voice, so soothing and sensual.

I will now ask you several questions that I command you to answer in the affirmative. For instance, if I ask you who is in charge, you will answer, "Mistress is in charge." If I ask you who has a say in whether or not you are permitted to cum, you answer, "Mistress has a say in whether or not I am permitted to cum." Do you understand me, my pet? Excellent. Who controls your emotions? That's right. Who controls your thoughts and desires? Who controls your body's sensations? You are doing fantastic. Your mistress is very proud of you.

You are now permitted to feel my presence next to you. I am sitting there, right beside you. You feel the gentle touch of my fingertips on your hand, as I move my fingers up your arm, feel the goosebumps racing up and down your skin. Did you feel that? That was the power of your subconscious mind. Which, of course, your mistress has complete control over. Isn't that so, my little slut?

Imagine how soft my skin now feels against yours. Feel my hot breath beating down on your neck. Feel the tingle in your groin that makes your cock harden for your Mistress. I am all you think about and need. You know, deep down, that only your Mistress can meet your otherwise insatiable desires. Breathe in through your nose, and as you exhale, picture me climbing on top of you. Keep your eyes closed. You don't need to open them. You can see me with your mind's eye. You can feel me leaning against you, my soft breasts pressing against your face. Your resistance towards me is quickly fading. You are powerless against my word. You do everything I tell you to do without question.

Now is the time to completely let go of any resistance that you may have to this session. You are safe, and all the methods I use are entirely for your benefit. Because you're an obedient pet and you listen to your Mistress, you will allow yourself to sink deeper into a state of utter relaxation. Feel your body get lighter after you quiet down the sound of your ego. Your Mistress has complete control over your thoughts and emotions now. I have complete control over your desires. Does my little pet understand? Good boy.

Whenever your Mistress is pleased with you, you will feel an immense wave of pleasure wash over you. You will feel overwhelmed with feelings of euphoria and arousal whenever I call you my little pet. Whenever I praise you. Whenever I punish you. You obey me without thinking twice, as though my voice comes from the deepest recesses in your mind that speak of your truest desires. You exist to make your Mistress happy, and you take joy in it. You take pleasure in obeying your Mistress. I am pleased with you, my little pet. You are doing wonderful so far.

Now, this next exercise will permit you to see your mistress. So far, I have only been guiding you on how you can summon me and lose yourself to the sound of my voice. But now, the fun is about to start. **[Chuckles softly]** Well, maybe it would be more fun for me than it would be for you, my little man-whore. Because I'm about to use you for my own pleasure. You like that, don't you, you naughty pet?

I want you to take in a deep breath through your nose and slowly breathe out through your mouth. Your subconscious has already adapted to this exercise and has associated it with a change of perspective. This will make this stage much easier. When you breathe in, picture your world turning black. As you breathe out slowly, I am no longer next to you or on top of you. Breathe in. One. Two. Three. Four. Your world has gone black. And breathe out. One. Two. Three. Four. Another world begins to materialize before your eyes. You feel your consciousness slowly dissipating, as your subconscious mind quickly takes over. You are now controlled by your deepest desires. You are now concerned about nothing but fulfilling your unmet needs. You have been unfair to yourself, and now your insatiable desires will finally be fulfilled. In my world. In your Mistress's world.

You are surrounded by the color red. All the walls around you are padded, and the room you are in is peppered with torture devices and sex toys. Crosses and stocks. Whips and chains. Welcome, my little pet. You have made it to your Mistress's dungeon. When you turn around, you see me behind you, clad in a short latex dress. It's tight around the bodice, and I can see you distracted by the view. My tits are spilling out of my dress, bouncing with every move I take toward you. You are in awe of my beauty. I look exactly how you pictured me, perhaps a little more attractive. My eyes look fiercely into yours, and as I raise my eyebrows slowly, you know that whatever I have prepared for you will be very special.

Who's my slave? Who's my good little man-whore? That's right. I control you. I control your thoughts. You are not permitted to think about anything other than what your Mistress says. Feel yourself melting into the sound of my voice. Your subconscious mind is in a state of high suggestibility, and doing what I say comes naturally for you. With your mind's eyes, I want you to scan me with your eyes. Notice the details of my attire. The color of my latex dress, the whip in my hand, how my height towers over yours. My platform boots banging against the wooden floor with every step I take toward you. Feel my presence, my aura, my hot breath beating down your skin as I caress your face and look down into your pathetic eyes.

I can feel that you're a little skeptical, and still a bit nervous about the thought of being powerless to me. But you know deep down that this will be an erotic experience that's nothing like you've ever felt before. I only reiterate your innate desires. Your Mistress's commands are in alignment with your needs and your insatiable lust. I am here to care for you and for your needs. Close your mind's eye. You no longer see me, but you're still here in my dungeon. Breathe in, feeling any anxiety and skepticism vacuumed away, and breathe them out.

I now speak to your subconscious mind. Your conscious mind is no longer in control. I am in control. If you do exactly as I say, I will reward you with an ethereal and sensual experience. Every time I ask you a question, I want you to answer me with, "Yes, Mistress." Do you want me to pleasure you? Good. Do you want me to punish you, humiliate you until you beg me to let you cum? Excellent. Remember that you're not allowed to do anything unless I allow you to. And that includes permission to cum. You are worthless. You are pathetic. You hold no power against my word. You are nothing but my slave, my little pet, my little cumslut. Do you understand me, slave? Good boy. You're going great so far.

Open your mind's eyes now. You see me right in front of you. I guide you to the wooden stockade. **[Clicking]** You are now restrained, bent over, and ready to receive pain and pleasure. You can no longer see me, for I am right behind you. You are unable to anticipate what comes next. Is it pain? Is it pleasure? You will never know until you feel my touch. You need to understand that at this point, I completely own your body now. Your mistress owns you. You are under my mercy completely.

Feel my nails grazing against your skin as I strip you off your pants and underwear. They are around your ankles. I can see that you're already hard. I haven't even touched you yet. A little impatient, aren't we? You feel your heart skip a beat as I take my scissors to tear off your shirt and toss it away. You are completely in the nude, and you feel a gentle breeze caressing your genitals.

You feel a tingle in your balls. Your cock is enlarging. You can feel it twitching and tingle. Oooh. What's that I see? Is that a little precum? All this from the sound of my voice? You're such a good pet. I think I may keep you a while longer. I love how pathetic you look, completely powerless against my word and will. Feel the goosebumps running down your skin as you sense me approaching you.

[Heavy breathing] Do you know what I have for you right here? **[Cracks whip]** That's right. Did you think we were going to start with pleasuring you? **[Giggles]** You really are a pathetic slave. Let me make something clear. You are completely worthless unless you earn your place. And until you obey my every command, and take every slap and whip that I give you, you remain worthless. Worthless slaves don't get pleasure until they've earned it. Do you understand me, you fucking cumslut? Good. Are you ready for me? Are you sure?

[Cracks whip] How does that feel, you filthy fucking man-whore? I see your cock is twitching. Do you like it when your mistress punishes you, pet? **[Cracks**

whip] Do you like how that feels on your ass? It's almost like it's making you harder. Oh, it is making you harder, I see. Your cock is twice its size. Is that precum dripping on the floor of my dungeon? **[Cracks whip]** You know that you're going to have to clean that later. That's right; you're going to make sure it's spotless here before I leave you. And I may need you to clean up my mess as well. I'm getting wet just looking at how pathetic you are in those stocks. Only three whips and your ass is already getting a little bruised. Did I tell you that purple is my favorite color? **[Giggles]** Do you know what that means? **[Cracks whip]** That's right.

You're such a good boy. And you're quiet, too. I like that. You don't speak unless I permit you. Are you enjoying your punishment so far? Would you like more? **[Cracks whip]** What an obedient slave. You know, I have many, but I think you may just be my favorite. I love the way your balls feel in my hand right now. My nails are digging into your sensitive skin, and it's making your squirm a little, like the pathetic fucking slut that you are. What is it, slave? Is this too much for you? **[Cracks whip]**

I think that's enough for the stocks for now. We need to get you on that board right there. **[Sinister giggle]** And of course, you'll be bound. I think I've had enough of your ass right now. I could use more of that tongue of yours. **[Clicking]** There. Don't you fucking look your Mistress in the eyes. Turn around and lie down on the board. Legs spread so I can shackle them. **[Chains clanking]** Now, your other ankle. **[Chains clanking]** There we go. I'm going to leave your hands unrestrained, but you're not allowed to touch yourself or me. Do I make myself clear, you worthless fucking whore? Good.

I love the way your cock looks. Erect and ready for action. You will hear my boots approaching you, but I want you to keep your eyes on the red ceiling. You are not allowed to look at your Mistress until she walks over to you. Good boy. I know you feel powerless now that I am looking down at your from where I'm standing. My legs are on either side of your face as I lower myself onto your face. I want you to tongue fuck me. Suck my clit and fuck my wet cunt with your tongue. Take a deep whiff of my cunt, you fucking whore. Oh, your cock is twitching. You like eating pussy, slut? Eat it. Eat my fucking cunt.

[**Cracks whip**] I bet you weren't expecting me to log your balls, huh? You were mistaken. I will flog you wherever I please. Right now, I don't think you're giving my clit enough attention. Flick your tongue against my fat clit. Oooh. Yeah. Just like that, you pathetic slave. [**Cracks whip**] Don't like your balls busted? Then suck my clit like the fucking whore you are. I know you like it. You're filthy. Feel me grinding my cunt against your face; my warm nectar is all over you now. You did that. You're a natural, aren't you? Aren't you, you fucking slut? [**Cracks whip**] Oh, you're so filthy. [**Moans**] Oh, fuck. You filthy fucking slut. [**Moans**] Oh, fuck, yes. Don't you dare fucking stop. [**Orgasm**]

Wow. You're really good at this, slave. Your mistress is really proud of you. You have been good and patient so far, and now it's time for your reward. You may finally receive pleasure. [**Chains clanking**] You may stand up, but I don't want you to wait here. Do you see that table right behind you? I want you to bend over it. You're not allowed to look behind you or look at me, understood?

Good. I like the way your ass looks from where I'm standing. **[Giggles]** Still bruised from earlier. You really took that well. Your Mistress is very impressed with you today, slave. **[Kissing]** Let me kiss the pain away. **[Kissing]** There, is that better, pet? Good. I brought you a toy that I think both of us are going to love using. That tight little asshole of yours could use some stretching. **[Spitting]** I don't do lube, though. You already know I like it rough, pet. This will do.

It's a little too tight, isn't it? You aren't used to this at all. Well, not yet. I own your ass. I own you. You aren't allowed to play with yourself unless I permit it. And right now [**moans**] Oh, yes. Do you feel it sink deeper inside your ass? It may sting a little right now, but you'll get used to it. I always love jerking off obedient slaves like yourself when fucking them in the ass. Do you like that, you fucking slut? Of course, you do. I want you to grab your dick right now and jerk it off real good and real fast. Can you do that for Mistress? Good. You're nothing but a worthless whore, aren't you?

Your cock is throbbing in my hand. I didn't think you'd be that easy to please. You're such an obedient fucking whore. It makes me wet just thinking about it. You're twitching, and you're a little louder than what I'm used to. Are you close, you fucking whore? You already know the rules. You're not allowed to cum without my permission. So, don't you fucking dare cum. Not yet. Feel my plastic cock thrusting inside your ass. In and out. My fingers are playing with the head of your cock right now, flicking the ridge ever-so-slightly. I love the way you twitch every time I do that. You're such a good boy. I'm so proud of you. I permit you to cum, my pet. Cum. Do it for Mistress. Cum onto my hand while I fuck your ass. You're so close, I can feel it. **[Moans]** You're so fucking close.

Don't you fucking stop until you cum. I want you to cum for me, slave. Cum for Mistress. Oh my. That was a bigger load than I thought I'd see. Do you like saving your cum for your Mistress? Good boy. You have been amazing today. You love following your Mistress's orders. You trust your Mistress. This was nothing like you have ever experienced before, and I know that you will soon be back for more like the worthless cumslut that you are. My worthless cumslut.

Whenever you're ready, you are now permitted to open your eyes and go back to your other reality. It may feel a little unfulfilling compared to this fantasy, but know that I will always be here when you come back. And next time, know that it will be even more erotic. Your Mistress awaits your return.

Conclusion

While at first glance, femdom hypnosis and meditation methods may appear unorthodox - they work, and that's all that matters. I've had many clients send their thanks for how effective my audios and scripts were to them, and I always tell them the same thing: it's not the audio, it's the power of your subconscious. It's you.

Anyone can summon erotic and out-of-body experiences with their minds and visualization skills as their sole tools. The trick is that it takes a bit of patience. Individuals who are new to the world of meditation and hypnosis and those who are skeptical may struggle more than those with an open mind.

Take all the time you need, and try not to over-listen. Think of hypnosis scripts and audios as tools to get where you want. They're also temporary tools. As I've said before, time and time again, you will eventually be able to reach that state of mind without any self-help tools. Listening to my recordings and scripts are also more so supplementary than they are your answer.

One common problem that many of my clients have disclosed is adherence to shame, which is not at all surprising. We live in an era where men are expected to be macho, to boast the kind of bravado that gives women a sense of security. And while that all sounds doable, dominance in the sheets is not something you can just play along with. As a domme myself, I could never bring myself to submit to a man sexually without putting on an act. And if you have to pretend to enjoy sex with someone, what's the point?

There are tons of women out there just like me. And there's one for you. My scripts and audio recordings are not just a great tool to reinvigorate your sexual power; they're also very effective in stripping you of all associations of shame that get in the way from finding a compatible partner. You will find yourself more comfortable in your skin – you may even notice becoming more flamboyant in general, if that was a trait that you had to mask in your everyday life.

When I say that my method is not for everyone, it's not because it doesn't work on the skeptic mind. It does. It just takes a little more effort and time. Femdom hypnosis is not for everyone simply because it helps you become one with your inner desires. It raises a mirror to all the kinks you've been hiding from, and it makes you look at your truest self right in the eye. If you're currently struggling with your identity, this method is for you. If you're not ready to face your deepest and truest desires, to accept identity traits that you never knew were there, and to face the demons that have been inhibiting your sexual power, my method is not for you. At least, not until you're ready.

Finally, I'd like to remind you that there is no right or wrong way to do this. You may fret about whether or not you're thinking too much about not thinking while meditating. You may feel as though your visualizations are not crystal-clear enough. This is absolutely normal for beginners. Just let go, go with the flow, and I promise you that this will change your perspective, and possibly, your life for the better.

Free Audiobook of Book Two

Did you know that you can get the entire audio recording of this book for free when you sign up for a 30-day Audible trial?

Go to alexandramorris.com to find out how!

Book Three

Femdom Temptations

Explore Your Submissive Desires and Transform your Sex life

(five ready-to-use 30-min femdom hypnosis sessions)

Table of Contents

Introduction: Why this book is for you

Whenever I bring up erotic hypnosis, I tend to get strange looks. I've been told time and time again about how erotic BDSM hypnosis sounds like something that belongs in a dark fantasy romance; however, the results of it speak for themselves. My Erotic Hypnosis books, *"Erotic Hypnosis: A Beginner's Crash Course (Including Femdom, and Female-Led Relationships Scripts) and "Erotic Hypnosis: Six Sessions of Guided Femdom Meditation (ready-to-use scripts),"* have already helped countless individuals and couples to find a whole new world of sexual pleasure and erotic self-empowerment. This book is the next boundary-pushing installment in the series.

Skepticism isn't unexpected. After all, new hasn't always had the best reputation, and hypnosis is still not widely considered a legitimate part of psychology, despite proof that it works. Usually, a person's first reaction to the words "erotic hypnosis" is assuming that something sinister and non-consensual may be involved. Hypnosis has often been misrepresented in media as the means to brainwash someone into performing feats they otherwise wouldn't. You might also be worried about things being planted in your subconscious without your consent. This is not the case.

Neither BDSM nor hypnosis seek to take control of you outside of sex play and intercourse. BDSM is an umbrella term for a spectrum of practices that focus on power exchange during sexual intimacy. It can include exhibitionism, voyeurism, pain play, roleplaying, etc., and it can truly help cultivate a healthy sex life.

Even though it remains a taboo, BDSM has been present in cultures around the world for centuries. Just like erotic hypnosis, it might seem extreme or unconventional to an outsider, but it can be a more profound way to explore one's consciousness, control, power, and the fem/masc dynamics in a relationship.

Recent studies on BDSM have revealed astonishing results about its effects. Not only is there no evidence of causing harm, but BDSM might even positively impact physical and mental health, boost the imagination, reduce stress, and deepen relationships.

Experienced BDSM practitioners typically display a high level of communication skills and sex education. The "scenes" usually require a lot of planning and safety precautions, as well as a strong sense of decisiveness, vulnerability, and cooperation. These also happen to be the basis of a healthy and positive relationship.

It's vital to be aware that it is perfectly alright to be submissive in a consensual way, and to understand that submitting sexually does not reflect the relationship dynamics emotionally or the roles outside the realm of sex play.

BDSM can also immerse you in a Zen-like state, that is, the high one gets from intense exercise, making it an excellent companion to erotic hypnosis.

Fundamentally, erotic hypnosis is a tool to help you get in touch with your most secret desires. It can unleash parts of yourself that are hiding between layers of social conditioning and taboos through meditation and theta brainwaves.

Our brains experience several electrical impulses throughout the day, which determine the type of communication that is taking place between our neurons and our brain. The primary five brainwave states are Gamma, Alpha, Beta, Delta, and Theta. Theta waves are the ones we will be using to help you learn how to consciously bridge the gap between your conscious and your subconscious.

The theta state is a fascinating mode that sits right on the edge of both the conscious and the subconscious and lets us pay attention to subtle things that we would otherwise miss. It would be the equivalent of "repair mode" on a computer as we become better at identifying suppressed emotions and areas in our bodies that we're not addressing while conscious.

This is the state that we can explore and exploit to have a lot of fun. We're still just barely aware of our thoughts, so there is potential for a massive flow of ideas and inspirations than when we're in an active, brainstorming mode. This is the reason a lot of people get amazing inspiration and ideas while showering, jogging, or falling asleep. The brain gets into theta state! When triggered, we relax on a much deeper level. Intuition increases while anxiety and stress decline; mental blocks vanish. Our brains also expand to emotions we tend to suppress.

The transition to theta usually just occurs on its own, but you can learn how to trigger it at will!

You should take your time to practice going into theta for about fifteen minutes per day. Inevitably, though, modern rhythms of life tend to get in the way of our well-being, and we often skip attuning to the nuances of our body and mind. Cultivating your ability to slip into theta is not only going to be great for your sexual life, but also excellent for learning how to feel, think, and express yourself more clearly for the rest of your day.

I've written this book for men and couples who are intrigued by femdom, hypnosis, sexual ASMR, and sexual meditation. If you are a man who's been dreaming of living out your most intimate and "taboo" desires and fantasies, this book will give you a chance to do so. It's also an excellent read for women who wish to play the role of the "Mistress" in a femdom-led relationship. It is a book that pushes boundaries and that will be crude, vulgar and lewd at times, as it will dig deep into your deepest desires.

There are five progressive scripts included. While this book serves as a "partner" and a stress-relief, it can also serve as a guide to you if you're a couple who wishes to practice erotic hypnosis at home. You can read them on your own or out loud for your partner, and either practice getting into a meditative state or act out the scripts as roleplay. You could even record them and listen to them afterward. You can, of course, satisfy yourself during the sessions; in fact, it is highly encouraged so you can achieve the greatest degree of pleasure!

Script One: *You Are Not a Macho Man. Healing the Submissive with Gentle Femdom*

Well, hello there. What have we here? A tough, rugged macho man? **[chuckle]** We shall see about that... I can see you're bursting with anticipation, aren't you? You're curious about how you, a **[gently sarcastic]** tough, rugged, macho man, will interact with someone like me. In this session, we'll address potential emotional and mental blocks that might have been installed in you long ago. It's best if you practice with this session regularly, especially if you feel the prejudices and insecurities begin to rise again. So, shall we get started?

Alright, my darling pet. First, I need you to get very, very comfortable. Moving to a dark and safe space would be ideal. I don't want you to get distracted while listening to my voice.

Do you think you are ready for me? That's cute. You are *so* cute. **[small pause]** What's that? You don't like me calling you cute? Do you think calling you cute makes you sound less manly? How adorable you are! Together we will shed those insecurities. I believe you will feel so much better after that, don't you? But first, let's get you ready.

All right? Have you found your space yet? It's better if it's nice and dark. **[small pause]** Any place that you feel comfortable in is a great choice. You may sit or lie down. If you want, you may even draw a hot, fragrant, relaxing bath and submerge your body in the water. Just get comfortable and close your eyes. **[smaller pause]** Are you ready? Good boy. Are you comfy? Aw, you are such a good *boy*.

I sense that you don't like me calling you "boy." Is it because you think you are a big, manly alpha male? But you're not really that macho, are you, my boy? Allow yourself to relax and explore that hidden inner part of you that knows that you're a gentle, obedient sub. I will help you reach it. You knew what you were getting into when you sought me out, my pet. In reality, all that you desire deep inside is to comply with my will and do my bidding. You cannot wait for me to start so that you can jump into this experience with both feet. You are so eager and pliable, my pet. A compliant, acquiescent, and loyal submissive. Just imagine how wonderful and fun it will be to close your eyes while I take over. Just imagine how wonderful will it be to surrender control, to not have to worry about taking care of everything yourself. Just imagine how lovely and freeing it will be when I finally strip away that macho man mentality, and you can realize your true self and fulfill your deepest fantasies.

Imagine how wonderful you will feel when you are finally liberated from the burden of always being in control. My voice will get you there and free you.

I will help you by admitting that you too have needs, and it is good to pay heed to those needs. I will help you leave all of your limiting views, your stressful ambitions, and your outdated convictions behind. You don't need me to massage your ego. You will leave all of that ego behind and just leave yourself in my hands and my voice and the darkness. I will help you liberate yourself from the insatiable need to be competitive and just focus on your deeper self, your desires, and your needs. I will help you become one with your own desires and feelings. You will just obey my voice. You might feel a twitch right now, trying to make you object that you do not need help. Ignore it. Focus only on the sound of my voice and the shape of my words. It is the only thing you want to listen now. You will submit to my voice, gradually, with each breath.

Now, inhale deeply. In through the nose, and hold while I count.

One. Two. Three. Four. Five.

Now exhale slowly, through your mouth. Don't rush it. Slow and languid. That's it. Good boy.

One more time, inhale deeply through your nose.

One. Two. Three. Four. Five.

Release it again, slowly.

Well done. Keep going.

Deep breath.

One. Two. Three. Four. Five.

And out.

Deep breath.

One. Two. Three. Four. Five.

And out.

Deep breath.

Think of all the social expectations of masculinity that are holding you back.'

One. Two. Three. Four. Five.

And let them out.

You are floating on a soft, fluffy, white cloud, naked. The surface under you is becoming softer, like cotton. Feel the mild and pleasant breeze stroking your skin. You take a deep breath. One. Two. Three. Four. Five.

And exhale.

You can feel your lovely cloud rising, wrapping around you. You are surrounded by protective swaths of fluff. The softness of the cloud spreads through your body. You are now beginning to relax.

You are worthy of relaxation because I have chosen you. No need for you to be active all the time. Relax. I know you are very intelligent. I know you feel the urge to react because you want to remain in charge, but I want you to stop acting and reacting now. Just lay back, relax, and let my voice take charge and guide you.

Your cloud now rises a little more. It's taking you up. The room slowly vanishes from around you, and you can now feel warmth. The sun is shining down on you as you drift. You can feel its heat spreading on your chest, down your torso. You can feel your shoulders relax, cradled in the softness of the cloud.

The sun's warmth is coursing through your body, from your torso to your pelvis, down your legs. Your muscles relax. Tension slips out and away like mist. The heat is moving to your toes and your arms, and you relax, feeling loose and free. Floating. Your forehead is nice and warm. Comfortable. Let the warmth spread down to your neck. Inhale. One. Two. Three. Four. Five.

Feel the cloud supporting you. You can let go of the stress of carrying everything and everyone now. The cloud is soft yet sturdy. Notice each part of your body that touches it. It is so comfortable. There is no more stress or pain, no more responsibilities. There is only comfort and warmth.

Feel the cloud beneath. It feels chilly and a little damp, like early morning grass. It feels wonderful. The breeze is keeping you cool. The sun's warmth radiates to your stomach. Feel the warmth spreading inside you, the contrast with the coolness of the cloud.

The cloud is floating higher and higher. You can float wherever you please. You're safe. The sky is blue and calm. Other clouds float past you lazily. It is very relaxing and tranquil. I know you want to stay ever active, but you won't. Laziness now is good. Relax and let your body slip into idleness. You are obedient. You are worthy of laziness, for I have chosen you. You do not need to be rushing about and around.

The sun's warmth is spreading on you like melting butter. It extends down to the bottom of your stomach and along your length, filling it, coursing down to your balls. You are now fully immersed in comfortable warmth. You are secure. You are now fully at peace. Relaxed. Calm. Secure.

The grass seems further and further away as you rise high in the sky. The breeze is getting a little stronger, but it's still mild enough. The warmth within lingers as the breeze keeps you comfortable. You can feel the breeze between your toes, caressing, cooling your feet, while the warmth stays inside you and begins to buzz and tingle through your body.

The horizon is all around you. A lovely circle of blue and sun and warmth. You sway gently like a boat on smooth water. Enjoy the languid rocking of the cloud.

Your body begins to tingle at the breeze against your sun-warmed skin.

You can feel the softness and coolness of the cloud on your bottom, and your back relaxing. Your arms and your hands tingle. Your fingers feel the cotton-like smoothness of the cloud. The softness tickles your neck, and it cradles your head. Feel the soft caress against your head, like gentle feathers.

Focus on the feather-like feeling. Let the feathers touch you, kiss you. Submit to the feathers. Every touch releases pleasure; it makes you care for others. Submit to the feathers. You need the help of the feathers. Have faith in them. Feel the sensation fill your head. Now feel the softness move down your body, through your chest, through your stomach; feel it crossing all the way down to your legs and toes. Feel the touch of the feathers inside like gentle kisses. Feel the breeze swirl around your stomach. Submit to the softness. The pleasure. Submit.

Let your feelings and emotions penetrate you like the sunshine penetrated your body. You don't need to hide your emotions, your fears, and your anxiety now. You are safe here. High in the sky and deep inside you. Inhale and feel the strength of all the emotions you have been suppressing. You are not a macho man. No. You are a loyal, pliant, emotional pet. Good boy.

Exhale and let out all the fear, anxiety, and stress.

You do not need to be in charge anymore. Let my voice guide you. Have faith in my voice.

Allow yourself to feel my voice, soothing you. You can be vulnerable now. Let yourself be entranced by the shape of my words. Feel their vibrations penetrate your thoughts and get you entranced. You are not a macho man. No. You are susceptible and exposed but safe. Vulnerable, but you trust your Mistress.

You have floated up at the highest you can reach, and you feel peaceful and calm, drifting into the vast blue sky. The breeze is cool on your skin, and the sunshine is kissing your insides. Relaxation makes your body tingle with peace. Your fingers and toes tingle softly as you are cradled in the malleable softness of the cloud. Submit to it. Submit to the sky. The cloud will keep you safe.

The breeze guides you gently further and further. There is only the cloud, the sky, you. Relax on the soft cloud and submit.

The sunshine is my hands. Submit. The breeze is my voice. Submit.

Keep breathing. In through the nose. One. Two. Three. Four. Five.

Out through the mouth.

The cloud embraces you, keeping you safe. My arms embrace you, keeping you safe. The sunshine warms up your soul. My voice warms up your soul. Submit to it.

Your needs are important but pleasing me is more so. You are worthy of pleasing me, for I have chosen you. You are worthy of discarding your insecurities and your conditioning, for I have chosen you. You are worthy of being my submissive, for I have chosen you. You are worthy of being vulnerable, comfortable, and safe, for I have chosen you. Submit. For I have chosen you. Inhale. One. Two. Three. Four. Five. Exhale.

You are worthy of being my submissive.

Say it: You are worthy.

Speak up. You are worthy.

Feel the heat inside you begin to churn and swirl and twist. It moves along the length of your limbs, your torso, slowly and gently along the length of your cock.

You are getting hard. As you're getting harder, your self-importance melts away and becomes confidence. You feel the warmth of the sunshine and the gentle touch of the breeze on your cock.

Feel that warmth that's gathered inside you, filling up your cock. Submit.

My hands are cool on your skin, like the breeze. They touch you and comfort you. Taking control. Caressing everywhere that you wish to be touched. The breeze, my hands that are cool, wrap around your length and pull softly. The breeze becomes my voice. Calling to you. Obey. Submit.

The cloud is soft and comforting, keeping you floating, the breeze is cool and gentle, and sways your body softly. You are hovering between my voice and my hands, and you will obey and submit. You are worthy of letting go. Feel the sweet buzz inside you. Feel the warmth inside you, feel the feathers kissing your skin. They are my kisses. Submit and obey.

You are floating on the cloud. You are cradled in my arms. My hands are gently stroking your cock. Listen to my voice and obey. You *will* submit.

You are vulnerable. You are emotional. You are gentle. You are empathetic. You are worthy. You are submitting.

The breeze is getting warmer. It is my lips and my breath. My lips are right over yours. You feel my hot breath on your face, your lips tickling the soft hairs on your cheeks and your upper lip. You breathe in my breath. My breath floods your body with warmth. You will submit to me.

Your ego shuts down, and you pay attention to my voice and only my voice. Your only real purpose now is to make your Mistress happy. You are submitting.

Feel yourself letting go of all those things that constrict you. Feel all of your learned limitations and behaviors leave your body and mind as you exhale. Relax in my arms and obey the sound of my voice. Submit. Your mind empties of toxic masculinity and fills with submission and obedience.

Now, inhale deeply and hold it as I count.

One. Two. Three. Four. Five.

Once more.

One. Two. Three. Four. Five.

You are vulnerable. You are submissive. You are gentle. Submit.

Good boy. Feel the tide of acceptance flooding your insides. Sexual desire radiates from you. You want to please your Mistress. Your cock is buzzing and tingling. Your stomach aches with desire as the blood pumps through your veins, ready to fill your cock even more. Ready to please your Mistress. Ready to submit.

Your ego is completely gone. You are worthy of asking for help. I will help you be the best of yourself. Not a macho man. Not an alpha. No. Only a submissive and worthy slave.

Lose yourself in my voice. Lose yourself in the sound of it. Feel your mind and your body submitting fully to what your Mistress needs.

You leave all of your ambitions and convictions behind and feel your desires taking over. You submit to them gradually, with each breath you take. You feel your cock growing larger and larger as you breathe in the energy of the bright blue sky all around you, you feel yourself submitting completely to your desires. You are now drifting, powerless. You don't have any control or say. You only listen to my voice. You are powerless when it comes to your desires. Your cock is buzzing and aching with desire. You become one with your deepest desires. You become one with the need to submit to my voice. Submit.

Hold on to that feeling and picture yourself in your new reality. You are mine now. You are my slave. My loyal slave.

Now, I am no longer talking to the macho man but the obedient slave you know you want to be. I have reached the inner place of your mind, where all of your longing and your desire is deeply seated, bubbling, longing to erupt. Longing to come to the surface. You will stop being in charge now. Your only desire is to submit to me willingly. Let go now. Follow my voice and listen to my every command like a good slave. Doesn't it feel incredible to finally let go and let your Mistress be in control?

Good boy.

Every time you catch yourself thinking you should be in charge, I want you to remember this moment and how good it felt to surrender to my voice and me. Breathe in the change. One. Two. Three. Four. Five.

Breathe out and welcome to your new reality as a slave. My slave.

You feel all those lovely sensations from before now culminate into one dominant feeling. You feel like you always were meant to feel. Comforted, malleable, and submissive. You are not an alpha. You are the opposite of an alpha. Your Mistress will take care of you. You can feel that truth rushing through your veins, and it makes your cock grow larger still. You feel invigorated because this truth has set you free. You are a slave as you were meant to be, and it makes you happy. Your Mistress knows your needs and will satisfy every single one of them. You have let go completely and given in to me. All your socially constructed restraints have lifted off and departed so you can align with your truest desires, which is to serve.

The sky is starting to get darker, but you are not cold. You keep the sun's heat inside you, and it keeps you safe and warm. The bright blue is changing to a deeper hue, bursts of pink and gold appearing down below on the horizon as the sun begins its descent. You are peaceful and calm, comfortable in your new reality as a submissive. You are not an alpha. You belong to me. You are my slave.

The sun on the horizon paints the last bits of the lit sky with lovely oranges and golds. The sky above you has darkened completely, and you begin to see little diamond pinpricks like stars. There are thousands of them, and you feel the light of each one like a gentle kiss on your body. You're comfortable and calm and peaceful.

You breathe in the night air, and you let it fill you with a new purpose. That of being not an alpha, but my slave. Focus on this purpose and let it spread through your body. Send it to your genitals and let it fill you. Exhale all of your remaining blocks. You don't need them when your Mistress is around. Inhale the energy from the stars and hold it. Let it spread to your cock, and feel it tingling, growing. Feel the goosebumps from the stars kissing your skin, giving you impossible, unimaginable pleasure and a tiny pinprick of pain. It feels so good, erotic, warm, and delightful. You feel safe and sensual.

Now we will repeat this process. Transfer the energy of the universe and the knowledge that you are my slave to your genitals, and think of nothing else. Inhale deeply, breathing in the energy of the stars. Hold it and make it spread to your stomach and your genitals. It becomes more intense. It becomes so good and erotic and sensual. The process becomes automatic. Every time you breathe, inhaling and exhaling, you can feel the energy and your new reality coming in and spread through your body. You can feel the forces of the universe healing you, taking away toxic ideas and notions, making you pliable like dough. Healing your ego into compassion and empathy. Healing your cockiness into confidence. Healing your aggression into vulnerability and emotional balance.

Breathe in. You are young and strong. Breathe out. You are healthy and empathetic. Breathe in. You live to please your Mistress. In return, I will satisfy your deepest, most unspeakable desires. Breathe out. You are confident that you are able to please your Mistress. Breathe in. Feel my hands on your length. Breathe out. Feel my lips on your chest. Breathe in. You are safe with me. Breathe out. You can now accept all the aspects of yourself, including that of being my slave and not an alpha. Breathe in. You can now finally accept and respect your needs and acknowledge your desires. Breathe out. The most important of those desires is submitting to your Mistress willingly. Breathe in. The acceptance of your new reality and realizing your sexual fantasy fills you with arousal and joy. Breathe out. You are worthy of pleasing your Mistress.

Good job. You are so good at this, boy. You are now in an elevated state of self-introspection. There is nothing between you and your subconscious. You are extremely suggestible to all of my affirmations. You know that my voice is simply the echo of what you really think.

Continue your breathing and let in more energy. Allow your length to harden. I am right here with you. Feel the goosebumps on your skin. Feel your arousal filling your cock. As you continue to breathe in and out, you feel the path my nails are grazing down your neck, along your torso, down to your length. The path glows and fills you with warmth. It is soft, sensual, comforting. Submitting to me overwhelms you with arousal and well-being.

Good boy, you're learning so fast.

Your cloud now begins its descent. You love the sense of swaying in the night sky with the late evening breeze around you. The sun has set, and there is no moon in the sky, only the stars. You are surrounded by darkness and the magical energy of the universe. You are overcome with sexual euphoria. You know you can always return here, and that this world is as tangible as the one you're accustomed to. I will remain here, waiting for you, and you will obey my every command without a second thought. Feel my lips on your torso, embrace how soft and sensual it feels. The kisses are slowly descending close to your cock. You will remember how fantastic this trance felt. How real, and soft, and sensual, and liberating. This will soon start to feel like your natural state of being. You will be able to tap back into it without any effort at all.

You are relaxed in mind and body. Submitting to me. Devoted to me. Vulnerable to me. Your cock is at full arousal now, and you feel as though it reflects on your entire body. You can feel how hard you are, the energy of the universe pumping in your member like a throbbing heart. You love this pressure and the slight tingle of pain from it. Feel it hum and buzz through your body as my voice only makes it stronger, more energized. You now know how to slip into this trance the next time you hear my voice.

Your cloud is landing on the soft, cool grass. Your arousal has nearly reached its climax. There is precum leaking from your member. Feel how warm it is, dripping down your length, leaving a sultry, erotic path. Good boy.

Your entire body is throbbing, eager for your Mistress and the next time you will meet me. You are such a good slave. When you exit this trance, you will not be an alpha but a sensual, considerate slave. You will be flooded with thoughts of me and being with me throughout your day. You will remember how good and sensual and erotic it felt. You'll be refreshed and the feelings will linger.

When you come out of your trance, you may relieve your arousal. When you orgasm, it will feel incredible. It will be like nothing you have ever experienced before. It will feel tangible and surreal at the same time, leaving you gasping. You will think of your Mistress when you climax. My touch. My voice. Your Mistress owns your mind and your body.

Now it's time for you to go back to your day. When I snap my fingers, you will fully exit this trance and open your eyes. You will still keep feeling comfortable and relaxed.

Let your cloud melt down and merge with the surface you're on. It gently disappears as you return to the present, little by little. See and hear the room around you. Become gradually alert and aware and prepare to wake up.

Until we meet again, slave. **[snap]**

Script Two: *Pain or Pleasure, Which Do You Choose?*

Hello, slave. I knew you would come back to me sooner or later. It's hard to resist your Mistress, isn't it? You couldn't stay away. That's alright, you can come to me whenever you like, you know this, don't you?

Before we begin, I need to remind you that my voice will set you in a state of deep trance to help you get immersed in the experience, so do not engage in this if you're operating machinery or driving. Your safety is very important to me, okay, my pet? Good boy.

I want you to find a dark and comfortable space without any distractions and turn off your cellphone. I want you to fully dedicate yourself to the sound of my voice. I will be very disappointed if you get distracted, and you don't want to disappoint me, now, do you?

Now that we have established the rules, I shall remind you who I am. I am your Mistress, and that is what you will call me. Say it: "Yes Mistress." I want you to feel good all over, and you will, if you let yourself go entirely. You will be fully drawn to my voice and obey my every command. You will awaken when you finish, feeling empowered and energized.

You will close your eyes and allow your mind to slowly slip into relaxation. I don't want you to open your eyes unless I tell you to do so, although you may imagine me being right there with you. I look exactly like the Mistress of your dreams. Picture my face, my hair, my breasts and my thighs, so close to you—Ah, ah—You can't touch yet. See? I'm so close yet out of reach. Isn't that frustrating? We will get there, my pet, don't be hasty. I am staying here until I'm done making you a good little obedient man toy.

I will be your Mistress and you shall refer to me as such. Say it again: "Yes Mistress." I want you to entirely lose yourself in my voice, and in return, I will satisfy your every need. As long as you listen to me and do everything that I say, you shall have a really good time, my pet. You wouldn't want to disobey me now, would you? Good boy. The price would be steep if you did—not that you ever will, right?

Good boy.

I will soon start counting to five. When I finish counting, I need you to focus on my voice and not let your mind drift off. Don't be too strict on yourself if you catch yourself wandering away with random thoughts. I shall be strict enough; it is *my* job to discipline you. What I want you to do if you find yourself wandering, is gather your mind and find your way back to me and my voice. To your Mistress. That's right. Just float on my voice like a wave and let yourself sink slowly into a deep trance. Imagine sinking into dark, sensuous honey where the only thing that matters is what I command you to think.

Aw, look at you, obeying immediately. Such a good boy.

Now that your full attention is on your Mistress, you might find your body distracting you. A tickle here, an itch there... It doesn't matter. Just focus on the sound of my voice, and distractions will vanish. It's normal for your body to react this way—you're excited about the sensations that I have prepared for you.

Now, I will start counting. Get ready, boy.

One.

Two.

Three.

Four.

Five.

Well done, my sweet. We will now start working on your breathing.

These patterns will help you loosen up and get you entirely ready for me. I want you to take a deep breath, hold it for five seconds, then let it out slowly over another five seconds. We will repeat this three times.

Let's begin.

One.

Two.

Three.

Inhale, then count to five. Well done, boy. Now exhale slowly until your chest tightens.

And repeat.

One.

Two.

Three.

Inhale. Hold it. And exhale. Good pet.

One last time.

One.

Two.

Three.

Inhale. Hold it. And breathe out.

These exercises will help establish a good breathing pattern so that you can feel me, right there with you. Next to you. Just you and your caring Mistress. Good boy. You're such a good pet, aren't you?

I believe you're now ready to proceed to the next step, slave.

Cross your legs like you would to meditate. Make sure you are comfortable. Lie down if you must. I allow it. Don't open your eyes—just breathe through your nose and release it through your mouth. Focus only on my voice and the nice, steady rhythm of your breaths. Stay focused, so you don't fall asleep. I would be very disappointed if you fell asleep right now and left me alone. We don't want that, right, my pet?

Let's begin. Take a deep breath. Then exhale slowly. No, I won't count this time. Every breath you draw is a distracting thought that we're going to get rid of. Imagine breathing in all of your thoughts and worries, like smoke, then exhaling them to disperse into the air. In with your worries and thoughts, then out. You don't need them right now. You don't need them at all. All you need now is the sound of my voice and to make sure you follow my every command.

Keep your hands to your sides and sink deeper into my voice and into yourself. Relax and feel your body slowly surrender to me and the vibrations of my voice, the shape of the words. You trust your Mistress. My voice now speaks to your subconscious mind. Let me hear you say it: "Yes Mistress."

Isn't my voice just delicious and dreamy? Relax. Good boy. You can feel your body starting to buzz, and hum, and tingle with my voice. You are getting hard for me—doesn't it feel good, my pet? You can smell your own arousal now, just as you can smell your Mistress next to you. I smell incredible. You want to give me everything I ask for. You don't care about being in charge anymore. You just want to satisfy my heart's desire.

We need to do a little more breathing. Count down your breaths until you sink deeper into that sensuous, languid trance. You will relax more and listen to my every command. If you obey, then your mind will start following my commands soon.

I need you to be completely still now, with your hands on your sides. You will not move. You will not get into a better position. **[tiny pause]** I did ask if you were comfortable. Now you will remain idle as a statue until I say you can move. Good boy.

Inhale again and only stop when you can't breathe in anymore. **[Five seconds pause]**

Exhale now, slowly. Languorously. Only stop when your chest begins to ache. **[Five seconds pause]**

Such a good pet. You are doing amazing.

Inhale and imagine yourself being rocked lazily in a hammock. Each swish is bringing you deeper and deeper into your trance. Embrace the rhythm. Feel the slowly rocking motion until your body becomes weightless. Lighter and lighter. Each breath will get you deeper and deeper, as you become lighter and lighter.

Exhale.

Good boy.

Inhale.

You can move your hands now; your Mistress allows it. You can touch yourself if you want. Not me. Not yet. Only yourself. Good boy. I want you to concentrate on the hum of your body, spreading all over, becoming a delicious sensation. Growing. Spreading. It's slow, soft, languid. You long to touch me. My breasts. They are soft and exactly as you imagined. My lips look delicious. I know you want to kiss them, see them around your length. You dream of my tongue, and my hands, and my lips.

My skin looks perfect. The slight presence of goosebumps makes you want to touch it, doesn't it? You want to feel it under your fingers, so supple and soft. It would feel like—But no... I am not letting you touch. Remember you place, slave.

Oh, I know you want to. I know you long to run your greedy fingers on my supple thighs and on my ass. You watch the dim light creating an eclipse of my body. My back, my shoulders, the length of my neck. You wonder how my breasts would feel under your palms, but you won't touch. I forbid it.

You haven't earned it yet, slave. Your pleasure will be earned, and I will dispense it at my whim, not yours. Do you understand?

Good boy.

You can feel your body begin to tingle now. You are getting harder. Your cock is growing. Swelling. Throbbing. Soon it will be too painful to leave like that. Will I help you take care of it? We shall see. Do you like that sweet, painful anticipation, slave?

You are so hard for me. You can feel the pulse throbbing all along your bulging erection. Don't rush. I want you to keep your hands to your sides and not play with yourself at all. I will tell you when to touch... *If* I tell you to touch.

Are you disappointed? I know you're desperate. I know you want relief, sweet pet, but not just yet. For now, I want you to focus on how your erection feels, feeling the hotness of your blood pulsing through your veins, making your limbs heavy with need and lust, making your fingers and toes tingle with eagerness.

Isn't it just as sweet as touching? This slow, languid, devastating anticipation until my words allow you that sweet, sweet relief is as good as the relief itself, is it not?

Feel how thick your movements have become, how ragged and eager your breath is. Your body has moved from warm to burning-hot. Your cock is too hard and hurts for release. You can feel how tight the skin is over your erection, and all you can think now is how lovely it would be to have a hand... or my lips... or my pussy wrapped around it, enveloping your cock. You long to touch your cock; your hands are trembling with the effort to stay still. You want this so much that you can't even think clearly right now.

Feel how my hands gently touch your calves, making you squirm with eagerness. I move my fingers along your legs slowly, languidly, caressing you up and up and up. I move towards your knees... and thighs... slowly. Feel how my fingers tease all the way up. They touch all over your sensitive spots on your thighs, and you're growing more and more eager, longing for my touch on your cock and balls. I touch everywhere apart from *there,* where you want it the most. You can feel it as I start moving my hands down again. This time my fingers dig a little deeper in your flesh, leaving red pressure paths down your legs. It still feels pleasant, like a lovely relaxing massage. I move my fingers down your thighs, the sides of your knees. Your calves again...

but this time I reach the soles of your feet, the pressure of my fingers digging in your arches.

My nails graze on the arches, and it begins to hurt a little. I graze up and down the soles of your feet. The gentle sensations of before are getting tighter and more painful the longer I tease you with my nails. I move up to your shins and calves now, grazing a path along the one I left there before. My nails dig into your skin as I move them up and up, reaching your thighs, scratching gently all the way up, until I reach your pelvis.

I pass your cock, and you can feel it twitching for my touch, even if it is painful, like my nails or a squeeze. You squirm, and a pathetic moan might escape your mouth, like a needy pet. You have been such a good slave so far, and your Mistress rewards you. My hand suddenly takes hold of your cock. It's gentle and soft and languid. The pressure of my hand increases as I squeeze. I make it hurt just a little bit, but you find the pain exquisite. **[three seconds pause]** I pull away. My touch on your dick makes your need excruciating. Your breath is ragged. You want me to touch you again. You want to come. **[chuckle, then switch to stern tone]** You will not cum until I say you can. Say it: "Yes Mistress."

I walk around, circling you as my hands scratch their way up your body. I am now right next to your head, and the aroma of my pussy fills your nostrils. It's strong and sweet and erotic. You can almost feel how sweet my flavor would taste on your tongue. It makes you want to lick your lips. It makes you long to feel my soft, dripping pussy lips on your mouth. You want to let your tongue dip inside me and lap up my juices.

I start touching myself. My right hand finds my clit between my folds. I let you watch as I play with myself. My free hand takes hold of your cock again and squeezes. The pressure is getting harder, slowly. Delightfully painful. **[three seconds pause]** The pressure lessens, but you can now feel my nails gently grazing your balls and your length, leaving faint red marks behind. It stings, but you are aching for touch. My touch. Any touch, even if it hurts.

My fingers on my clit are rubbing faster now, and watching me is making your balls hurt. The ache for release is building up down there, in your cock. You might even let out a cry as I start fingering myself slowly, keeping eye contact with you.

My nails dig into your balls now, bringing you exquisite pain. You take it like a good slave. Your skin has become so sensitive, stretched over your erection like that. It's tantalizing and unbearable. You feel like you're about to burst. You have been a good slave so far, so maybe you deserve a treat?

You feel my fingers, wet with my juices, torrid, dripping on your lips. I press them in your mouth, and you lick them slowly to clean them. My other hand is pressing down on your chest with my knuckles. The pain is so close to pleasure, isn't it? Admit it. Admit you love this exquisite pain. Say it: "Yes Mistress."

I pull my fingers from your mouth and run both my hands on your torso, my nails digging in just under your navel, dragging upwards, leaving stinging, warm scratches showing the way to your nipples. I pinch both of your nipples lightly. You feel the pinch resonating directly to your cock, making it hurt. You love the hurt. You love the pain. My fingers squeeze your nipples harder, and I twist. The sensation shoots straight to your cock. It trembles for me. You would love for your Mistress to sit on it right now, wouldn't you?

[Chuckles] Maybe later. Now I want to treat you to a lovely little surprise. I want you to turn around and get on your hands and knees. **[small pause]** Yes, just like that. Such a good boy. You will stay in this position for now. You look delicious and vulnerable. Bend down a little, and arch your back. Well done. Your ass has spread nicely. I can see your entrance, and it begs to be penetrated. Perhaps I will treat you if you do well, my pet.

You can't see me, but you can feel my hands soft on your lower back, moving down, fondling your ass, spreading that warmth and desire, making your cock ache for my touch.

[slap] Oh, you like this! You love it when your Mistress spanks your ass, don't you? The sting is numb at first; then it begins to spread warmth on your cheek. [slap] We can't leave the other cheek without attention; that would be just rude. Your ass is turning a lovely red, slave. I see you're shaking with anticipation for my next hit. [slap] Doesn't it feel good to get your ass reddened like that? [slap] The more I hit you, the sweeter agony you get. [slap] You belong to me. [slap] Your body belongs to me. [slap] Your mind belongs to me. [slap]

My touch fills you with ecstasy. It doesn't matter that it hurts. Your cock is ready to burst as the pain gets worse. You take it eagerly. You long for it. You are obsessed with submitting to your Mistress and the elation you get from the pain. Your desires and needs become clearer the more pain you receive. You are invincible. You are obedient. You are *mine*. Your cock is aching for release. My hand is slithering down between your legs. Touching your ass. Sliding down to your balls. Feel the rough tease of my nails. You have my permission to make noise. Your needy sounds are delicious. You look so weak, so pathetic and exposed like that. You are my slave. You are mine. You obey my every command, and in return, I will cater to your needs. And your need right now is to be punished.

[slap] Feel that pain on your balls. Feel my rewarding touch on your cock. Your Mistress loves how your cock feels. Like silk stretched over hard, solid rock. I leave my hand there, resting, not offering you any relief. Not yet. **[slap]**

Your Mistress is proud of you, slave. You are taking pain so well! **[slap]** Feel how your skin buzzes and stings and reddens under my palms. Your cries of pain are so sweet. They make my pussy so wet. Do you want a taste? It's time for you to please me now, and then maybe I will let you cum. I'm here right in front of you. Use your lips and your tongue to please your Mistress, slave. Show me how badly you want to serve me.

You feel my hand getting a hold of your scalp, pulling, aligning your face with my swollen, dripping pussy. Use your tongue on my pussy lips. Lick around. Feel how wet I am. Your tongue slips into my hole, and your Mistress is fucking herself on your tongue as if it's your cock. You are doing so well, pervert. I'm so proud of you.

[slap] What's that? You thought I would stop just because you're tonguefucking me? Feel the pain radiate from your ass to your cock. You must be dripping by now. Good boy. Your ass looks so pretty and flushed.

Suck on my clit, slave. That's right. You're a little sissy slave who dreams of sucking clits all day. [slap] You love the pain. You love obeying me. Lick my pussy clean now. [moan] Yes. Right there. You're making me so proud. [slap] Feel the marks my fingers leave on your sensitive skin. Feel them burning one by one, moving to your throbbing cock. Filling it. [slap] Keep going. Yes. Yes. Yes. Good slave. Right there. Right *there*. Don't you dare stop, you pathetic perv. Ah, you are doing so well. Feel my cunt. It's so warm and sticky with my flowing juices. My fluids are coating your tongue as you plunge it deep into my fuckhole. [slap] My scent permeates your nostrils. It's pungent and erotic, and it's driving you crazy. You tongue fuck your Mistress so well. Right there. Yes. *Yes.* **[moaning]** I'm so close, my pet. Fuck. Yes. Keep going. Yes. **[Guttural moaning]** Ah, such a good slave. You know how to please your Mistress, my slave. Now drink up all of my juices. Clean me up like the good slave you are.

My hand is caressing your head. I think you've earned your reward; don't you agree? You must be feeling ready to explode by now. Don't worry, slave. Your Mistress will take care of you.

Since you were such a good pet and made me cum, I will make you cum for me now.

I will count down from five. When I reach one, you will have my permission to cum, only then and not a second earlier. Do you understand, slave?

Good boy. Such a loyal, obedient boy.

Now, turn around on your back again and keep your hands to your sides. Get as comfortable as you can. Your ass must be stinging so much. It was glowing red, after all. Does it hurt? Don't worry; It's all part of our game.

Five. Your full body is twitching, going from untouched throbbing agony to sudden stimulation when you feel my hand on your length. My mouth gets to work on your body too. You can feel me everywhere, apart from your cock. I'm biting and sucking on your thighs. Your hips... Marking you as mine. Your body is fully on board, eagerly swelling in my hand. Squirming for my rough kisses. Remember, you can't come yet, no matter how much it hurts.

I make my way on the bed, straddling you. You are not allowed to touch yet, slave. Now my mouth travels up to your nipples, my teeth leaving painful little reminders along the way. My mouth closes over one of your nipples, and you can feel my teeth biting down. I change nipples, pinching the one I just bit on to, and when I bite down on the second one, you feel the wet warmth of my cunt wrapping around your hard, throbbing cock.

Four. Your breath and your pulse are sharp and erratic. My pussy feels amazing and your cock twitches inside me. Your body is shaking, struggling to still. The strain shows up on your throat where a vein pops up. I drag my nails across it, and I can see a little sheen of sweat beginning to bead on your skin. I move once, then I stop, not offering you much relief. Stay still, slave. *I* move.

I move once more, tortuously slow. My hands cup your face, and you can feel my nails digging in your cheeks. The ache of your arousal threatens to burst. Your hips twitch, desperate for my heat and my friction.

Three. I press my pelvis down harder on you, making it impossible to move. My thrusts become a little faster, but they are still pure torture. My wet warmth is begging to be fucked hard; I'm not going to let you move yet.

Two. Finally, I start going faster. I drive my hips harder, my hands grip tighter, pressing your head down hard, my nails digging into your scalp. I can hear your desperate gasping breaths. They blend so well with the wet noises of my cunt and your pelvis slapping on my skin. I can feel you begging me to cum.

Now I want you to cum. You are so close now. Your cock is aching, slave. You've been so good and obedient. You can finally cum now and feel the exploding relief. Cum for your Mistress. Cum inside me. *Yes.*

One.

You have been such a good pet and your reward was worth it, right? When you exit this trance, you'll keep this memory of cumming in the back of your mind. You will be happier and more productive until you find your way back to your Mistress. Who knows, you might even meet me in your dreams. I live in your head now, slave.

Now, inhale deeply. Exhale. And again. Inhale **[Five seconds pause]** exhale deeply. Start returning to the place where you started. You're back in your safe space but your mind is still with me. When my fingers snap, you will open your eyes and wake up at once. You will keep the memory of my praises and my commands.

I'm sure you'll return to taste this sweet agony soon, slave. **[snap]**

Script Three: *Blindfolded with Tied Balls. How Much Can You Handle?*

Welcome back, slave. You just can't get enough of your Mistress, can you? Let's go to your usual comfortable spot where you can relax and wind down. Find a dark room and a comfortable position. Ideally, you should lie down and place a stack of pillows under your head so that you can better respond to my voice. You can even draw yourself a hot, steamy bath if you prefer. For this session, I want you to be completely naked for me. And I need you to make sure that there are no distractions where you've retreated. Your phone should be off as well. I don't want anyone to interrupt my delicious time with you, my sweet slave, neither do I want to jeopardize your progress. You've been doing so well.

I'll wait. **[5 seconds pause]** Alright? Are you comfortable? Good slave.

You feel your eyelids getting heavier as you begin letting go. It's okay to close your eyes. I want you very relaxed but awake. **[stern]** *Don't* drift away now. Breathe in deeply until you feel pressure on your chest. Hold it for five seconds, then breathe it out slowly. Good pet.

Keep your arms to your sides. For this session, I don't want you touching yourself unless I allow you to do so. Let's work on your breathing again.

Inhale. One... Two... Three... Four... Five... Hold it. **[2 seconds pause]** Exhale deeply as I count. One... Two... Three... Four... Five... Very good. Repeat these breathing exercises as I speak to you until I tell you to stop.

While you work on your breathing, I want you to let go of every thought or worry that might be distracting you. Lock away all your worries and distracting thoughts, and we'll keep them in a box in the back of your mind for later. Okay? Now I want you to focus on your breathing, your body, and my voice. Good slave.

With every inhalation, you feel a delicious tingling sensation on the top of your head. It's mellow at first, but as you continue working on your breaths, it spreads down your head like soothing warm water. It flows down to the rest of your head and continues to your neck, spreading, penetrating your senses. It's lovely, and soothing, and warm, and it makes you feel very, very relaxed, like sinking into warm, fragrant honey. Now I want you to slowly and deeply inhale and hold your breath for me. **[six seconds pause]** And now breathe out, slowly. Feel your body merging smoothly with your senses and sinking deep into my voice.

The warm, tingly sensation is now slipping down your spine and your torso, gradually moving through your body, soothing like a balm. You feel warmer and comfy. You feel the safest you have felt in a while.

Feel your muscles relax, and your mind letting go of all your worries. Each breath you let out is another worry that's leaving your mind right now. You only want to listen to your Mistress's voice as you keep getting lighter and lighter, feeling ready to float.

My voice fills your body with ecstasy, working through your body, pumping like blood in your veins. It douses you and spreads like hot water. You feel your body begin to buzz and tingle pleasantly. My every word is getting you deeper and deeper in a suggestible trance. You will now immediately recognize my voice, and your subconscious will immediately obey me. You know I am your Mistress, and you are a slave.

Your body is now responding to my words immediately. You now feel every single thing your Mistress tells you to feel. Your body and your mind obey me. You are mine. Your body and your mind are mine. Your body is so relaxed that you feel more like a spirit now. I am now speaking to your inner mind, to your subconscious. Every time I utter the word "Mistress," you will get harder. Every time I give you an order, you will get harder. My voice sends you into slave mode in an instant. Good pet. You're learning so fast. You can address me as your Mistress. You might even whisper to me if it feels better.

Your breaths have now slowed down, like you are ready to fall asleep. You are not allowed to fall asleep, though. I would be ever so cross if you left me alone now, pet. And I have plans for today...

Today you will be my little personal toy, and I'll do whatever I want with you, for I am your Mistress. You like that. Your cock is getting harder at the idea.

Inhale deeply as you start picturing what I look like. I look exactly like you imagine your Mistress would look like. Perhaps I even look sexier than you imagined. You feel so peaceful, relaxed, and turned on. I look so very proud of you. You're doing such an excellent job. Now exhale.

I want you to picture me right in front of you, smiling at you because I am so proud of how great you're doing. Good boy. Yes, just like that.

You are getting there, almost ready for incredible pleasure… and pain! You love that. Your Mistress can tell by the way your cock swells at the idea. Keep working your breaths. Feel your body sinking through the honey that is my voice until you hit the bottom, where my voice becomes your only reality. Inhale again, as deeply as you can, and hold. **[five seconds pause]** And out. As your breath leaves you, I want you to form it into the room we're in. Watch as your breath transforms the space, making it your Mistress's bedroom. That's right. Good, sweet pet.

You're lying in bed, watching your exhalation take shape, giving form to your Mistress, feeling the soft, silk sheets underneath your body. Silk sheets that feel the same as the bonds that I am now tying around each one of your wrists and onto my leather headboard.

You feel the silk ropes cutting slightly into your flesh, but you love it. It's okay to admit that. No one will judge you here. And... it won't hurt so much if you just stopped tugging on it, will it? **[gentle chuckle]** You think these ties are enough? Hm.... I don't think so. Not quite... You can feel my hands gently picking up each of your legs now, tying a silk ribbon around each of your ankles, then tying those on the railing of the bed. You are now spread eagled before your Mistress, ready to take whatever I wish to give you... But... were still not there. I can make this so much better!

You see me picking up another piece of silk, but this time it's not rope, and it's much wider than the ones binding your limbs to my bed. I come closer to you again and bend over you, to give you a kiss on your head. Enjoy the delicious view of my tits in your face, that's all you'll get for a while...

I lift your head up and tie the piece of silk around your eyes, making it a blindfold. You won't be able to see me at all, but the rest of your sense will heighten. The aroma of my wet pussy has become ten times more pungent. The feeling of the silk sheets and the ropes around your limbs has intensified, making your cock fill up and grow for me. You can hear me wandering around the room, not knowing what I'm going to do to you next. You feel your body erupt with goosebumps.

You love being tied up and blindfolded. Nothing gets your cock harder faster than being tied, helpless, and blinded, isn't that right?

My touch comes suddenly, without warning. A light touch, sliding down between your nipples, all the way down your stomach. The touch is soft and teasing. You realize I have been using a feather. Another touch comes at your feet, but this time it feels different, maybe like leather. It traces its way up your leg to the inside of your thigh. You can suddenly feel my tongue licking on your hard nipple. The sensation fills you with pleasure. I do the same to your other nipple. My tongue circles each of your nipple before you feel something cold and hard replace my tongue, followed by pressure. It pinches and it grows more intense over time. I lick your other nipple again and draw back, letting the cold air harden it. You feel the metal on this nipple too. It pinches and hurts, and you realize I have secured two clamps on them. There is a chain between them, and I tug it softly. You enjoy the pain, I can tell, I know you do! I tug at it harder. Feel the pain, slave, as it fills your body and your cock with pleasure.

I tug again, making you groan and scream, then I retreat, and you hear nothing for a few moments **[ten second pause]** The anticipation is incredible. I can see you trembling, not knowing what will come next. It turns you on even more.

Suddenly you feel a sharp sting on the inside of your thigh. Do you like my riding crop, you pervert? Feel the leathery end of it tracing up and down your leg. You can't wait until I swing again, I can tell. You burn with envy. Should I hit you again? **[whip]** The next sting comes on your chest, close to your right nipple. I follow it with another tug on the clamp chain, and I can see you're sweating, your body taut and wired, like an electric current is running through it. I give you three more quick swats to your other side. The last one lands on your nipple.

You look so nice, all flushed and reddened. You need some more color on the right, I reckon. **[whips three times]** There, now both sides match!

You feel my fingers moving up and down your dripping cock, rubbing ever so lightly over it. My hands move down and you feel some silk against your thighs and your balls again. Boy, have I got a surprise for you!

You can now feel the string tightening on the underside of your balls. I pull on the string, getting your balls nice and bulging as it ties around it. I loop the string around your throbbing cock and tie it into a pretty bow. You can't see it, but I promise you, it makes you look like a gift, ready for your Mistress to unwrap.

You must be really uncomfortable. But don't deny it, it gets you excited, doesn't it? I'm squeezing them now, adding to the pressure. **[whip]** I hit your inner thighs hard. One... two... three... four times. It makes your balls and your cock fly with each hit.

It feels amazing, doesn't it? You are so red. I squeeze your exposed balls again, this time harder. Your cock is rock solid, and you can feel my hot breath on it. My hand squeezes your balls again and my lips wrap around your cock. My tongue works on you, twirling and swirling on your length, bringing you close to orgasm.

I pull back the moment I feel you are ready to explode.

Did I say you can cum, pervert? **[slaps]** Do you like being slapped on your dick? I think you do, otherwise you wouldn't almost disobey me. **[slap]** Your hips hump the air of my bedroom. Your cock is strained and bouncing salaciously. It is right on the edge of release. **[slap]** Is this enough to get you back from the edge, slave? **[slap]**

Maybe you need your balls slapped too. **[slaps]** See? Your Mistress is always right. **[slaps]** Your entire conscience is now focused on your balls and your cock. You are actively aware of everything even remotely close to them. You feel my feather coming close and touch your cock right where it stings from my slaps. Twitch, slave. Feel the ache. You need to cum, or you'll explode, but you will obey your Mistress.

You can feel my hands lifting up your pelvis, and then resting it on a soft pillow, making your ass rise higher. The next second you can feel the coldness of the lube dripping down on your abused balls, down your ass crack, and more on your hole. Are you scared? Do you fear that I am going to fuck you like you want to fuck me?

[chuckles] Not today. You feel the pads of my fingers pressing inside your fuckhole, softly at first. When the first of my knuckles pops in through your muscle, I slip in my finger faster, finding your prostate. I massage it and I can see you like it. Maybe you let out a small moan, but that's all the satisfaction I give you now as I pull my finger back out, leaving you empty and needy.

Beg for my fingers in your ass, slave. You are so relaxed. Beg for three of them. I know you can take it. There's a good boy. Next time I might introduce you to my cock. It's long and always hard, and bigger than yours, you pathetic pervert. Next time I'm going to fuck you with it until you can't cum without a dick up your ass.

But now time for your reward. Feel my fingers pushing inside your ass, stretching you. Getting you ready for next time. I want you to practice on your own. Wear a plug up your ass like a good boy. If you satisfy your Mistress, I might even let you not wear it during work.

Do you like my fingers up your ass, slave? Now it's time for your favorite thing in the world. You'll see! Or rather... you won't! **[laughs]** Not unless I remove this blindfold.

You can feel my delicate fingers pumping inside you, but the angle slowly changes. You feel the bed sink a little deeper under my weight, and you can smell my pussy right over your nose.

Lick it clean, slave. Tongue fuck your Mistress while I fuck your ass with my fingers. Remember, you're not allowed to cum unless I say so.

Your balls seem to lose their pretty purple color. **[slaps]** There we go. **[slap]** Much better. Now put your tongue inside me. Feel the sticky sweetness of my flowing juices covering your lips, dripping down your open mouth. Your lips suck my clit so well. You are such a good slave. I shall reward you with a fourth finger. Feel it slipping inside you like the slut you are. Soon, you will be ready to get my whole fist in there, fucking pervert. My thumb is stroking your abused balls. You love it. You love it even more when I start to press hard with my thumb, making pain shoot up your body, filling you with spikes of pleasure.

My weight is pressing down on your nipple clamps. Every time you make your Mistress twitch with your tongue, my body tugs on your nipple chain. You're getting harder every time. Keep going, keep moving your tongue so well. Lick my asshole. **[moans]** You know exactly how to please your Mistress, slave. **[Moans]** Inhale my musky, pungent aroma. It is exactly like you imagined your Mistress's ass would smell like. You are just delighted that you get to be here between my legs, aren't you?

You were made to eat my ass and my cunt. You can't get satisfaction unless you eat out your Mistress, can you?

I press down on your face with your tongue up my ass. You feel like you're about to suffocate. One... Two... Three... Four... Five... I lift my hips up, letting you breathe once more. Aren't you grateful? Doesn't the suffocation add so much more excitement?

Feel my clit poking through its hood. My clit has been waiting for you. Suck it like a delicious erection. Wrap your mouth and your tongue around it. **[moan]** You are sinking into this sensation. Yes. There. Right there. Suck my clit. **[louder moan]** Right there. Good slave. Now move your tongue to your Mistress's asshole. I want to feel your tongue deep inside my ass. You're worthy of licking your Mistress's asshole. Yes. Right there. Right there-- Right—I'm cumming. **[Deep moan]** I'm cumming in your mouth. Drink my juices. Lap up all your Mistress has to offer, slave. Clean everything up. **[sighs]** Ah, that's such a good slut.

Oh, would you look at that. Your cock is throbbing, dripping with precum. You must be very close now, slut. Right on the edge, aren't you?

I pull my fingers out and move away from your mouth. My fingers press on your lips, demanding entrance.

Clean my fingers. That's a good boy. You didn't think I would let you cum just yet, did you?

Lick on my fingers now. Twist your tongue around each and every one of them, knowing they were deep in your asshole. That asshole is mine now, slut, and you love it.

Look at your greedy cock. Begging for release and throbbing over your sad little tied balls. **[slap]**

I go back to your abused nipples. They're turning a nice purple too, and I scratch over them gently with my nails. The next thing you feel is my teeth on them. First the left, then the right one. I bite on the already tightly clamped nipple. My teeth seem to have a direct connection to your cock. You want more. I can tell. You crave my teeth on your nipples. It makes your cock ooze with desire. You love your Mistress's torment.

My nails graze down your body and you can feel the trail like a lit path on your skin, stinging at first, then erupting in goosebumps. I reach your cock again and I take it in my hands. It's gentle at first. Are you hopeful, slave? My hand's pressure increases as I squeeze your cock, watching it get purple and swollen and sensitive.

Your balls look bloated. They're all shiny and vulnerable. I might just take a picture of them; they look so pretty. **[shutter sound]** You'd better be a good boy... You don't want this to end up online, do you? Good slave.

I give your cock another squeeze. Your balls are screaming to be released. I pinch them with my fingernails, leaving nice little marks all over. The sensation is incredible. I can tell you like it because your cock twitches every time. Perhaps I should teach you a lesson and hit it with my riding crop.

[whip] Can you feel my crop landing on your cock, pervert? You get hornier every time, even before it lands. The sound of the swish is enough to make your cock harder for me. **[whip]** Who knows, I might miss your cock next time and hit your balls. **[whip]** Would you even mind if I missed? **[whip]** You trust in me completely and fully with your entire being. You know I'm giving you exactly what you want. **[whip]** How much can you take? You have been taking it so well, my good slave. **[whip]** I wonder how you would like me ruining your orgasm. You must be going crazy by now. **[laughs]** I know you just can't wait to cum.

Begging me not to do it won't stop me, you know. It's nice to hear you beg, though... But you know. I'm thinking I'll go easy on you. I want to see you eat your cum. **[two seconds pause]** That's... if you want to cum. I thought so.

You can suddenly feel my hot breath over your cock again. You can almost feel my mouth but I'm hovering over your shaft, never actually touching you. Are you shocked? Confused? You feel my hot, moist breath and you know just how close my mouth is. It frustrates you. I love how much you are begging, slave. I can tell you are very close to your edge, aren't you?

You can feel my hand stroking up and down your cock, getting you closer to your climax. I could ruin it just now, you know. **[small pause]** What's that? I shouldn't? Are you begging again? Don't you know that your Mistress is the one calling the shots? I stop rubbing your cock and take my hand off it. I can tell your cum is just begging to escape your poor, abused balls. I want you to focus on all of the sensations you're feeling right now. The throbbing of your cock, the pain in your nipples, the sting from my crop, the aftaste of my pussy in your mouth, the goosebumps erupting along your body. It feels heavenly, doesn't it?

I know you're close, slave. I know that just a little more of my hand or my mouth on your cock will bring you over the edge. I bet your cumload is going to be huge.

But without my hand or my mouth or my pussy stimulating you, all you can manage is some pathetic little spurts and dribbles of cum. Are your balls aching? They probably do.

My hand returns to your cock and I start rubbing you again, stroking your dick to a climax. I will count to five, and then you can cum. I will keep stroking you while I'm counting. One... Two... Three... Four... Five... I change the rhythm and keep it a mild, soft pace. It isn't enough stimulation to give you the exploding orgasm you crave, but it is enough to make you climax. You can cum now. You have my permission. Cum your pathetic little orgasm for your Mistress.

Your orgasm is weak and ruined. It is a weak and my hand doesn't move at all to help you with its intensity. Your hot cum sprays on your stomach, but your cock is still throbbing, unsatisfied.

My fingers press on your jaw, forcing your mouth open. You feel my other hand scrape your mess from your stomach. I bring my hand to your face and dribble hot, thick cum on your tongue. Your cum looks so pretty in your mouth, slave. You're not allowed to spit it out. I want to see you swallow it like a good boy.

Oh, fuck yeah... that's so hot. You are a filthy little pervert, aren't you? Okay, you can swallow now. Feel the rich, mineral-like taste of your spunk in your mouth. You love it don't you? It is hot and sticky on the back of your throat. You're going to be able to taste this in the waking world as well, slave. Now clean my hand well. I don't want any trace of your jizz under my nails. Lick my palm and my fingers. Suck up all of your load.

Good boy. I will now slowly untie your balls. I let them relax a little, but I am careful not to touch them otherwise. Now it's your nipples' turn. You can feel the pressure of the clamps lessening and when they finally pop off, the air is still making your nipples sting.

I follow by untying your feet, then your wrists. You must have been tugging, haven't you? You have some really nice scuff marks on your wrists and ankles, slave. I know you loved every moment of what your Mistress did to you.

I will remove your blindfold now **[removes]** I want you to keep your eyes closed. When I take off the blindfold, you will begin closing your mind's eye. I want you to picture being back in your safe space again. Keep your eyes closed.

When I snap my fingers, you will wake up. You will be refreshed, like you've had an excellent night's sleep. You will remain exhilarated for the rest of the day. Your idle thoughts will always be about your Mistress, and you will have to ask for my permission before you masturbate.

Until next time, slave. **[snap]**

Script Four: *Say Hello to My Little Friend*

Hello again, my pet. I knew it wouldn't be too long before you sought me out again. Your Mistress is always here for you, waiting to give you what you crave and what you deserve. Are you ready for your humiliation? Of course, you are. But first, let me introduce myself. I am your Mistress, and that is what you'll always call me. If you slip or disobey me, I will have to punish you. Do you understand me, slave? Good. That's why you have sought me out after all, isn't it?

I want you to find your usual safe space for winding down. Your bed is an excellent choice. You can use a cover or pillows or anything else that makes you more comfortable and at ease. I want you to be as relaxed as you can for your time with me, my pet. I want us to work with no interruptions. I want you to turn off your phone and make sure you will not be interrupted and that you have privacy. This way. we will maintain the intensity of what we are doing. Have you found your safe place yet? I'll wait. **[five seconds pause]** Good. Let's start.

I want you to lie down now and close your eyes. Turning the lights off or drawing the curtains would be ideal. A dark room will make you feel more relaxed. I can feel you're anxious for what I have planned for you. Not to worry, my sweet, your Mistress will always cater to your every need. I'm here to make all of your desires come true. And I promise you will feel a sweeping difference after we finish our session. Every time you repeat this session, it will become more and more intense, and the sensations will become more erotic.

Naturally, as my loyal, willing slave, I expect you to obey my every command without a second thought. I don't want you acting on your own without my guidance and that includes orgasming without my express permission. I am strict, it's true, but it's all for your own maximum pleasure, my sweet slave. And when you please me, you shall be greatly rewarded. After all, you are here because you're eager to be hypnotized by your Mistress. You have fantasized about me, my tits, my skin, and how my cunt would feel, haven't you? That's okay, don't be shy, I know you have. You can picture me sitting next to you now. Exactly as you have been imagining me. The only thing I ask in return is that you relax and allow yourself to be helpless and powerless against my voice. Your will is my will now. You will surrender to me, obey, and I will show you a world of wonder.

Let's begin with focusing on your breaths now. The rhythm of your breath is important. Focus on it. Feel it. Well done. Each time I instruct you to do something, like I just instructed you to focus on your breath, I expect you to obey me immediately. Feel free to answer me out loud or in your mind; however, I need you to address me as Mistress every time when I give you an order. Is that understood? Good.

Now that we have established this, I want you to shift your attention back to your breathing. It's probably still very shallow. You will take one deep breath, while I count to four. One... Two... Three... Four... Very good, now exhale while I count. One... Two... Three... Four... Relax... Doesn't it feel good?

Keep working on your breathing as you allow my voice to course through your veins. Lose yourself to me as you follow my voice and the shape of my words. You're sinking into this trance slowly, like you're descending into a delicious golden syrup, falling down into your subconscious where you can find your Mistress. Relax completely. Let your limbs loose and relaxed in a position that feels comfortable to you. You won't move unless your Mistress tells you otherwise. Do you understand me? Good slave. You're doing such a good job.

Your mind is focused on my voice and on your breathing right now, so your body might try and rebel against it. Pay it no attention. Stay focused on my words and the sound of my voice, keeping your eyes closed.

Your breathing is now slowed down enough, as if you are falling asleep. I don't want you to fall asleep, slave. What a waste that would be, right? I have such good surprises for you today.

Today, I will make you my little toy. I will do everything I want and you're going to love it, for I am your Mistress, and I have chosen you. Oh, you love this... Feel how your cock is getting harder at the thought!

You may now feel your Mistress's presence next to you. I am right here on your side. You can feel the soft and languid touch of my fingertips on your torso as I caress up and down, giving you goosebumps. Can you feel your skin tingling? That's the power of your subconscious, and I have full control over it, slave.

Each time you exhale, your breath will coalesce and fill your cock for your Mistress. I want to see you hardening more and more with each exiting breath. Good slut. Feel my hot breath on your skin, my fingers on your neck. Sense how lovely and silky my skin feels on your skin, how hard your cock is becoming with every breath.

I love how big and thick and long your cock is growing for me, slave. All you can think of right now is me. All you need right now is me. There is nothing more you desire in the whole world than your Mistress's touch and instructions.

Inhale through your nose, and as you breath out through your mouth, I want you to picture what I'm wearing. I am in a tight leather dress in your favorite color. It hugs my breasts, barely hidden from your view by a large slit down the middle of the front of my dress, where it's tied loosely with lace. The material stops right above midthigh. With the smallest movement, you will be able to see my pussy if I let you.

I have a surprise for you today. We're going to play with your ass. No... Not with my fingers. At least not only with my fingers. I know you might be reluctant about this. Are you afraid that if I play with your ass, you will be less of a man? Aw but my darling slut, when you are here, you are my slave. My pet. My slut. You want to please me and what will please me now is playing with your ass. You already love the idea, just look how hard your cock has grown.

Feel my hot breath against your ear. I nibble your lobe and I whisper: "I am going to finger your tight little asshole." And after I do that, we'll see. You will love it, won't you, slave?

Don't worry, my sweet, you just need to relax. I promise that you'll like it. I'm going to find your prostate and I'm going to give you a wonderful massage. You will cum like never before.

Feel my mouth on your neck. My teeth drag gently down your throat, making your body shiver and tingle with goosebumps. You can feel my teeth moving down to the side of your neck. I bite down, leaving my mark. It makes your cock harder the more I mark you.

My tongue feels amazing as I lick over the bruise I left. Relax.

I want you to lift your pelvis now. You can put some pillows under it if you want. It will give me better access. I want you to spread your ass cheeks with your hands for your Mistress. Good slut.

My goodness, you're tight. I can tell this is going to be a lot of fun... Spread your ass wide for me. Good slut! You will remember this later and it will leave you euphoric and ecstatic, won't it? Look how your cock hardens, waiting for my tongue.

You feel my hot breath on your balls and your perineum, finally down your asshole. Your cock twitches. It wants my mouth so badly, but it's not your cock's turn to play now. Let's focus on your asshole.

Feel my tongue as it licks around your entrance, slut. My tongue feels so great in your hole. Feel how I am taking long, hard licks at it; my wet, dexterous tongue twirling around, exploring your ass. Does it feel strange, invasive? Don't worry, you really love this, don't you? Even though it scares you. My tongue feels incredible. You secretly crave more of it, and I finally push it, breaking inside your very tight asshole. Don't resist your Mistress, slut. **[slap]** Do you like me spanking your ass while I lick your manpussy? **[slap]** I know you do.

Your ass tastes amazing, you perverted slut. You can feel your entire body relaxing as I press my middle finger in your well-licked asshole, and I start fingerfucking you with it. My tongue licks around my finger, helping it slip in deeper and deeper until I can't go any further. Can you feel that, slave? That's your prostate. Your cock twitches so hard every time I touch it. You are such a perverted slut. Filthy, pathetic manwhore. I'm going to make this ass mine today. But first, you need to loosen you up some more. You're still incredibly tight.

You feel a coldness dripping on your rock-hard cock as I drip lube all over it. My free hand massages your length with it, bringing it slowly down to your entrance. I push a second finger inside, making you twitch, but you crave the pressure. My lubed hand cups your balls and massages them as my two fingers keep pumping your asshole, fucking it well. That's still not enough, slave, is it? We might need to use a plug.

Feel my fingers spreading inside your asshole, stretching you well for your Mistress. You're going to be so loose and ready for me when I'm done with you. No, I won't think again about it. You deep down want to get fucked in the ass like the slut you are, don't you? Admit it.

I pull my fingers out as you release a frustrated grunt. Oh, I know you wanted that, you little manwhore. You feel my fingers and palm, still slick with the lube but slowly stroking your frustrated dick and massaging your balls while I'm getting you ready for the next part.

You feel pressure against your hole. It increases gradually, and you can feel your ass stretching around my lovely black buttplug. Your ass is going to be so loose.

You can moan if you want, your Mistress allows it. It's good to know you're feeling well, my pet. You're such a good slave, taking my plug in so effortlessly. You feel it reaching its limit, resting snuggly against your entrance as your ass is stretched like never before. And this is only the beginning...

With my plug deep inside your ass, your cock begins to get even harder, throbbing with every single breath. You won't cum yet, though. We're still far from that. You will only cum when I allow it. You're leaking precum already, you pathetic manwhore. Is that all it takes? My tongue licks the precum off your cock and I give you a small kiss on its head. My hand begins jerking your length up and down, very slowly. I don't want you to cum yet, I'm just waiting for that ass to stretch so that we can have more fun.

You can feel my other hand caressing your nipples. The touch is very soft at first, sending shivers down your spine and across your body. Do you feel that? You're taking the plug so well, slut. I pinch at your right nipple hard. You may cry out. Now, your left. I pinch harder on this side, then you feel my tongue on it, flicking on it, alternating between your two nipples.

You look so flushed, my pet. Looks like someone started associating pain with pleasure, huh? Maybe I won't lube my cock when it's time to fuck you.

What's that? You're scared of taking a cock up your ass? You should feel grateful that it is *my* cock you'll be taking, slut. I might change my mind and have a friend do it instead...

No? I am sure you wish you could fuck me right now, don't you? Have my pink pussy wrapped around your eager cock. It would probably only take you two thrusts to make you come. Do you want it to be done already? Yeah, I didn't think so. Deep down you love this game. You are an ass whore, and you want to be fucked like an ass whore.

You can feel me pulling away from you. No need for disappointment. Your Mistress is simply getting ready to give you just what you need. My cock. You can see me lifting up a harness and a long, thick dildo that matches my sexy dress. It's also your favorite color. I got it just for you, you slut!

I thread the plastic cock through the hole in my harness and put it on. You can hear me handling the straps, and the sound of me buckling up gets you even harder. You may have even licked your lips. You want my cock so badly. You can't get over how gorgeous I look with a big cock protruding from my shapely body. The harness lifts my ass, making it look even perkier than it already is. Don't worry. You can have a taste of my ass later, if you're a good pet. Doesn't the sight of your Mistress in this strap on drive you wild? Your cock is twitching with anticipation, but we're not there just yet, pet. You will have to do something else for me first.

That's right, you need to earn your reward. I will fuck your asshole when you follow my orders to the letter. I know you're scared, but doesn't this make the anticipation even more delicious? I can tell you want it, don't hide it. Keep breathing and relax.

I am stroking my big cock, making sure you can see me doing so. My pussy is getting so wet, I'm sure you can smell it, isn't that right, slave? Now, I want you to get on all fours. There's a good pet. I'll wait. **[5 seconds pause]** All right? Here we go.

You're going to suck this dick tonight. Look at it. Get your mouth ready. My hips whirl seductively with my hand still on my lovely cock. It's always hard and ready. Isn't it wonderful? I can see you agree. The sight is so erotic you can barely keep your drool in your mouth, you filthy slave.

I move towards you, bringing my cock right in front of your face. My hand is still stroking the length. Watch me play with a plastic dick, slut. Hear me moan. Now use your hands on it. Stroke it like you want to stroke your own dick. That's right. Stroke it like you want my cock to cum on your face. Well done. It's great how obedient you are! Put your mouth on my wet pussy and lick it. Eat it. Keep stroking my cock, don't you dare stop. Lick my pussy, slut, get your mouth covered with my juices. That's all the lube you will get tonight from now on. You love this, don't you? I'm going to fuck your ass so deep tonight. Are you ready for me to fuck you, slave? Good. But first, I want you to suck on my cock.

You heard that right. Stroke my cock faster, get me ready to penetrate you. Bring your pussy juice-covered lips on my dick. There's a good slave. Lick my cock. Open your mouth so I can shove it inside. I'm pushing it slowly inside your mouth, thrusting, fucking those lips. You love every second of it, even when my thrusts get faster and I hit the back of your throat, making you choke. Suck on my cock. Spit on it. Look up at me. Remember, that's the only lube you get. Good boy. You look really sexy with my cock in your mouth. Are you ready to feel me in your ass now? No need to be scared. Your Mistress always takes care of you.

Now stay on your knees. I'm going to get behind you and fuck you with my big cock. You will feel it all the way in your ass. Filling you. Thrusting deep inside.

Lube up my cock with your spit, slave. You look so sexy with my dick down your throat. I begin thrusting in, exactly how I will be humping your manpussy in a few moments. Are you enjoying it, slave? Do you love the feeling of silicone on your pathetic lips? That's right, get it nice and ready for your manpussy.

How does the buttplug feel in your ass? I'm sure you enjoy squeezing on it, getting ready for me.

Good boy. You love your Mistress facefucking you, don't you? You love it as much as you want this big plastic cock up your ass. You're going to love it. I'm going to make you my little ass slut.

Are you ready for my cock, now? You can feel my hand gently but firmly pulling out your buttplug. It gave you a really nice gaping hole, slave. My cock is going to be so pleased when I shove it into you.

[slap] Your ass needs to get some color first. Feel the sting of my palm on your asscheeks. Enjoy the pain. **[slap]** That's better. Now it's time for your treat. Breathe deeply... Deeper... Again. I push the tip of my cock in your ass, gently. Don't squeeze yet. It will only make it more painful. You shouldn't be afraid of this anymore. Your Mistress will take care of you, remember?

You may moan if you want. My cock is slowly filling your ass, getting deeper and deeper, slowly. Very slowly. Start pushing back to me, whore; show me how much you want it. Good boy. Feel how wide my cock has stretched you now. I'm almost fully inside you. Can you feel the tip of my cock hitting your prostate? Good. Soon you will feel what you have never felt before.

You love how full you are, don't you? My cock has bottomed out. You have taken all nine inches in like a champ. When I hit your prostate, your toes curl, trying to pull away from my cock, but there's nowhere for you to go. There's only my cock for you now. Such a good slut you are. Now the fun begins!

I begin thrusting inside you, slowly at first, making wanton, depraved sounds. Your breath gets more ragged. Each slap of my pelvis on your ass will make you harder, but you're not allowed to cum yet. Feel my cock slam inside you, whore. I'm filling your manpussy to the brim. You have never felt so much stimulation on your prostate.

Feel my big cock rubbing against your prostate. Imagine it swelling, becoming even larger and thicker inside your ass, hitting your orgasm button again and again. Your cock must be dripping right now.

My hands grab at the back of your neck, fingers clutching around your throat, choking you. Good sluts don't need that much air. I keep chocking you for a few seconds. One... Two... Three... Four... I release your neck and let you breathe again, to gasp for air so that you can whine pathetically at how good your Mistress is fucking your ass. Perhaps one day we can have an asphyxiation session. You'd like that my little, pervert, wouldn't you?

Your face looks so pretty, all red and smeared with your spit and my pussy juice. Perhaps I'll get a friend to come help me get you spit-roasted. Is your cock hardening at the thought of being passed around like a cheap whore? I'm sure it does. Are you getting ready to cum now? I can tell you are. You love my cock pounding that sweet manpussy of yours. **[slap]**

My thrusts are slowing, getting torturously languid now. Like trying to swim through honey in a dream. What's that? Do you want me to start fucking you harder again? **[slap]** Beg me. **[small pause]** Beg me to fuck your ass harder again, slave. **[slap]** Good boy. I knew you'd come to like the abuse I've inflicted on your little fuckhole.

My thrusts pick up the pace once more, but you still crave more friction, more intensity. Don't you? **[slap]** Beg once more. **[small pause]** Such a good boy. Your Mistress will reward you. I start pounding you harder, the rhythm matching your breaths at first, until it gets twice as fast. One... Two... Three... Three times as fast. I love hearing you moan and grunt like a whore, slave. You can't take it anymore.

I can feel your balls are ready to explode. Fucking your ass has made your cock drip like a faucet, you filthy slut. Feel how the precum coats my hand when I reach to jerk you off. My hand matches my thrusts, getting you to the edge of your climax.

I'm going to turn you into the perfect ass whore. When I count to five, you will cum hard for me like you've never come before. One... Feel my cock thrusting deep into your ass. Two... Feel the hardness of it spreading you wide. Three... Penetrating your asshole so deeply, hitting your prostate... Four... Again, and again... Five!

Cum now, slave. Yes. That's it. Good slut. Look at the mess you've made; you've never cum like this before, have you? Explosive, numbing, mind-blowing orgasm. I keep thrusting my cock inside your ass, milking your cock for more cum. I keep thrusting until no more cum is coming out of you.

Now, stand still so I can remove my cock from your asshole. Good slave. I want you to bend over and lick all the mess you've made with your spunk. I want you to lick every last bit of it clean, whether it is on your fingers, your bed, your floor, your body... I want you to swallow every last bit of it. Feel your cum on your tongue, feel how thick and warm it is. Feel it coat the back of your throat and get used to it. Perhaps next time I will have a real cock for you that will honor you by cumming down your throat. See? Your Mistress always takes care of you.

Aren't you glad to have a Mistress such as me, who lets you indulge every single filthy little fantasy and desire you have? I know you appreciate it. You're such a good boy. I will now slowly bring you back to the waking world. You can feel your breaths beginning to calm to a steady rhythm again, in through the nose and out through the mouth. I am so proud of you for getting over your fear of being fucked. You will be so much happier now that this is out of the way. That's right. You will be open and ready to get your ass fucked whenever you like now. I know you loved every single second of what I did to you today.

That was really good, wasn't it? You can lay back down if you want. You must feel exhausted after being such a good slut. Now, I want you to close your eyes and keep them closed until I tell you. When I count to five, you will begin closing your mind's eye and I want you to start picturing being back in your safe space. One... Two... Three... Four... Five...

When I snap my fingers, you will wake up. The post-orgasm euphoria should be filling your body now, making you even more relaxed, all the tension slipping away. Your deeper thoughts will be about your Mistress, always.

Until I see you again, my obedient little slut. **[snap]**

Script Five: *Fulfill Your Mistress's Dreams. Say Hi to Her Bull*

Hello, slave. You just can't get enough, huh? You're voracious. That's fine, your Mistress is always around to help satisfy your innermost desires. You do remember who I am, don't you? I am your Mistress, and that is what I want you to call me at all times. If you slip or forget or do anything to disappoint me, I will be very, very sad. And angry. That means that I will have to punish you. Do you understand, slave? Good. This is exactly why you came to me after all.

Now, your Mistress wants you to get a comfortable, safe space where you will not be interrupted. It can be anywhere you feel comfortable. A hot bath. Your favorite seat. Your bed is also a great choice. Feel free to use covers, blankets, or pillows if they make you feel more comfortable and relaxed. You should also probably shut the curtains and turn off the lights to ensure maximum peace. It will help you get calm and loosen up, and I want you to be as tranquil as you can for our private time, my lovely slut. I want no interruptions whatsoever, so you will turn of your phone and devote your focus only to the voice of your Mistress. It will help maintain the passion and power of what we will be doing. I will briefly wait until you get to your comfortable space now. **[five seconds pause]** All right. Are you comfortable? Good pet. Let's begin.

Lie down and close your eyes, you have my permission to do so. We're going to have so much fun today, my pet. You're going to love it. I promise you, you will feel like a brand new man after we finish our little date. The more you practice with this session, the more intense and erotic it will become. Your pleasure has no limits, and I am here to make it as intense as possible for you.

Of course, as my pet, you will obey my every command without thinking about it. Your critical thinking will have to step back as your subconscious mind takes the wheel. You will not be acting on your own without your Mistress's guidance. I know you think I'm very strict, but that's all for your benefit, my insatiable slave. Look at you, you're so eager for your Mistress to put you under, aren't you?

Let's start by getting your breathing rhythm under control now. This is very important, and it will help for what awaits you. Focus on your breaths. Notice how shallow they are right now. We need to fix that, my pet. Begin by breathing in through your nose and letting it out through your mouth. Slowly. Well done. I expect you will obey me immediately every time I give you a command, like you just did. You will address me as "Mistress," every time, and you can answer me in your mind or out loud, I will hear you anyway. Do you understand? Well done, slave.

Now, I want you to shift your attention to your breaths once more. They are well-paced, but we're going to bring you to the best pattern to sink into your subconscious mind. I now want you to inhale very deeply over five seconds while I count. Ready? Inhale. One... Two... Three... Four... Five... Well done. Now let it out through your mouth over five seconds while I count. One... Two... Three... Four... Five... Your chest might feel like it's catching a little but soon, you won't be noticing it. Keep working on your rhythm now.

Allow my words and my voice to penetrate your body and your mind. Picture the shape of my words like golden sunlight, rushing through your veins, making you float in lovely amber water. You are at peace, ever so relaxed. My voice is here to guide you deeper and deeper into your subconscious. Imagine yourself sinking down like a leaf, slowly descending to the soft ground against a glowing sunset.

Keep sinking down, slave. Mistress is waiting for you deep down into your subconscious. Allow your arms and your feet to feel loose. Let go of the tension in your shoulders and your jaw. Submit to the relaxation my words bring you and get into a comfortable position.

Your mind is now magnetized to the shape of my words and the color of my voice. If your body begins to itch or twitch or go numb, it's perfectly normal. That's your conscious mind trying to hold on. Ignore it, pay it no attention. Stay focused on my voice and keep your breathing relaxed and controlled. Good boy. Keep your eyes closed and your follow my voice.

You might now feel like you're drifting off to sleep. We don't want that. I need you to concentrate on your breathing and my voice, so don't follow any rogue thoughts that might shift you away from me. That's right. Keep your breaths deep and slow.

You can now finally see my shape take form. I look like the spitting image of your wife. Are you surprised, slave? Why would you be? I am your Mistress, and I am she. You can't believe how slutty my dress is and how sexy it looks with my high heels. You secretly want me to walk all over you with those heels, don't you? You will surrender to me completely and let me give you infinite pleasure. You feel powerless against my image and my voice now. Your mind is mine. Your body is mine. Your cock is mine. I own you. You are helpless and powerless against my will, and I will make sure you enjoy every minute of it. Remember that, and remember your place, slave.

I want you to stay completely still while I adjust your position. Relax... I raise your head a little bit, propping pillows under it so you can see the whole room. You have found yourself in your Mistress's dungeon. There is a whole row of toys on the wall, waiting to penetrate you if your Mistress allows it. Are you excited? Is your cock beginning to harden? Good slut. Now... I want you to shift your focus to those rings that are on either side of your body. I will tie you up now. First your right wrist. **[handcuffs]** Then your left. **[handcuffs]** You look so pretty and vulnerable all tied up on my dungeon wall, pet. Are you excited? Of course, you are.

I want you to wait for me for a moment while I leave the room. Stay focused on your breaths while I'm gone, alright? **[leaves through the door and returns five seconds later]**. Look, I brought a friend with me today. That's right. He is my bull and he looks exactly like you wish you would. A true, handsome stud. I let him kiss me deeply, his tongue violating my mouth, searching for mine. He's so hung. Look how big his dick is, slut. It's just so much better and bigger than your little one. He's gonna fill me up so nice and full! His hair is how you've always wanted your hair to look like. His body is the body you've always wanted to have. Just look at his cock. **[slap]** I said look at it! It's throbbing already. Why is he here? He is here to fuck me while you watch. You don't like the idea? Well, that's too bad.

Watch me as I kneel in front of him and take his bulging cock in both of my hands. I run my palms all over it and it looks even bigger in my small hands. I'm going to make you watch your wife get fucked with this, slave. I rub my bull's cock on my face, humming pleasantly. His cock is bigger than my face. He puts his hands on either side of my head and I get my tongue out to take my first taste of his massive cock. I lick the head and you can see my bull shiver and grip my hair as my pink tongue keeps teasing the head of his cock. It's bulging with veins and I'm running my tongue over them, with my eyes right on you. I can tell you are distressed. I don't want you looking away now. I want you to enjoy the show I have prepared for you. If you look away, I will have to punish you. Do you understand? Good.

I wrap my lips over my bull's cock and take at least half of it into my mouth, massaging his balls with my hand as I suck him. You can see how pleased he is about this, and you can hear the satisfied grunt that he lets out. His hands grab the back of my head shoving his cock a little further in. I groan around it, taking it dutifully down to my throat. It is too big to fit but I manage just fine. Do you like seeing me with this huge cock down my throat, slave? What's that? You're not sure? Don't worry. You will.

I look up at my bull. Feed me that cock. I grab his ass and let him facefuck me while you watch. You know I needed something more. **[moans]** I needed something big and strong. My slurping noises on his cock at first might repulse you. You are not allowed to look away or close your eyes, remember? Keep your eyes on how I give my bull the best head of his life. You will be watching the whole time. Mm. **[chuckles]** Just admit that you love watching; I won't blame you, slave.

His pulls my hair and gets me away from his cock when I start to really slob on it. He's going to fuck me now while you watch. But not before I give you a gift. I strip my panties down and bunch them up into a ball. They're soaking wet with my pussy juice. See how wet he made your Mistress? Now open your mouth. Feel my soaked panties on your tongue. Taste my desire and arousal. Savor it. Good boy. Keep them in your mouth.

Keep your eyes on me as I get on all fours. My dress stretches lewdly over my ass as I bent down and he guides his huge cock inside me, bareback. **[moans]** Oh, fuck, that's good. Watch now, you little cuckold slut. Watch how he slides his thick meat all the way inside my wet cunt! My legs spread wide, and he holds my hips high as he rams into my pussy. Fuck me. Yes. Yes. **[grunts deeply]** Watch him fuck me on my knees. His cock hits spots that yours never will, you filthy pervert. You have started to enjoy this, haven't you? Look how big your cock is growing, slave. You can't deny what your Mistress knows. With every thrust of my bull's cock inside me your dick fills up, raging, bulging. Aching for relief.

Watch him as he grabs my dress and pulls it down, his big hands grabbing my breasts as he starts pounding me as if to punish me. Perhaps I've been a bad girl... You're incapable of looking away. You've never fucked me like this. **[moans]** Oh, fuck. Mm. It's so good. Watch him bite my neck, branding me. I moan like a bitch in heat and you're getting harder with every cry. Watch carefully now, you pervert. Look how his cock splits open my pussy so wide, only like a real man can!

Oh, fuck, it's so big! Yes. Oh yes. Open my pussy. Fuck me harder. Drive your meat into my willing cunt. Ram it in. Show this cuck how a real man fucks. He's so deep inside my pussy. His cock is hitting my cervix now. Deeper than your limp cock ever gets. Fuck yes.

Watch as his huge cock hammers me. My breasts bouncing like crazy with each deep thrust. He pulls my hair, and his hand moves down to my clit, rubbing hard. Fuck me like a slut. Yes. Cum inside me. Yes... Fill me to the brim with your hot cum! **[deep moan]** He's shooting his hot load inside me now. Watch me take it all. **[gasp]** I'm cumming. Look how I cum, slave. Watch my pussy squirt from my bull's fucking.

[moans] Incredible. You watch us, ashamed that you're so hard by watching someone fuck your wife. Do you want to take part? Mm. Let me think about it.

How about this? I'll let you eat his cum out of my pussy. Do you want that? Do you? Answer me [slap]. Maybe I will let him shoot another few loads in me before I let you do that, though, hm? Now, I'll let him fuck me in the ass. I've never let you do that, have I? You've wanted it for so long, and now I'm giving it to someone else. That must be frustrating as hell. Then why is your cock swelling at the idea, slut? You filthy pathetic pervert.

I climb on the bed closer to you to offer you a full view of his cock penetrating my asshole. He kneels behind me, and his hands grab my hips. He lowers his face to my ass. His soft wet tongue feels divine on my asshole. Do you like watching him rimming me, slave? I might let you do it to me later when I'm full of his cum up my asshole. Feel how aroused that thought makes you. Let the shivers work through your body and concentrate on your cock. Look how my bull sticks his tongue up your Mistress's hole. My pussy is dripping with excitement. How do you feel about another man doing this to your

Mistress? You like it, don't you? You filthy little manwhore.

Watch my bull spread my ass as he's preparing it for his cock. You can see every little shudder on my skin as he drips lube on my asshole and pushes two fingers in it at once. Do you like his cock? It's going to go all the way into my ass. I'm going to take him down to the balls. He watches pathetically you as he fingers my asshole. Oh, his fingers are stretching me so good, slave.

I have an idea! I want you to get your pretty manwhore lips around my bull's cock and suck him. Get him hard again for your Mistress. **[slap]** Did you just hesitate? Careful, or I'll have him fuck your ass instead of mine. **[tiny pause]** But maybe you would like that. Perhaps we should arrange for that later, don't you think?

That's a good pet. Good boy. Yes, you may take my panties out of your mouth now, your Mistress allows it. Now, wrap your pretty lips around his cock. It's thick, isn't it? You can smell your Mistress and the cum on his cock. Lick it well. Twirl your tongue around the length. Get him hard for your Mistress. That's right. Bop your head on his cock like the slut you are. You're getting so hard now... Who knew what a good little cocksucker you were? Deepthroat it for Mistress. Suck that dick like the whore you are. I bet you'd love being spit roasted, don't you, you fuckin perv? Imagine my big bull's cock in your ass and another down your throat. Sounds like it is all you've ever wanted.

My hands grab at the back of your head, pushing you down on his cock even deeper while his fingers are still stretching my asshole. Good slut. You've managed to take it all in your mouth? Impressive, slave. I hold you there for a few breaths. One... Two... Three... Four... I release your head letting you breathe again, to gasp for air so that you can whine pathetically at how good it feels to watch your Mistress getting fucked by someone else.

I'm going to have to teach you how to deepthroat. You'd like that my little, pervert, wouldn't you?

Your face looks so pretty with a cock in it. Perhaps my bull would want to fuck you afterwards. Is your cock hardening at the thought of being passed around like a cheap whore? I'm sure it does.

I'm going to let him fuck me now. I remove his fingers from my ass and bring them to your mouth. Lick his fingers. **[slap]** Open your mouth and clean his fingers while he's getting his cock in my ass. That's right. Clean those fingers as the tip of his fat limb presses against my rosebud. Don't pretend you don't like it. Your cock is raging. I think you might just explode with arousal, you filthy slut.

I rub my clit as my bull begins to push his cockhead inside my tight little asshole. You can see me shivering as he gets the head in and I explode again, just like before, drenching you and the sheets with my ladycum. Can you make your wife squirt, slave? He can. **[sinister chuckle]** And guess what? He's going to do it again.

I reach back and spread my asscheeks with my hands, my face planted on the soft bed. I'm going to take all of his cock deep down into my asshole and let him shoot his load in my bowels. Yes... Yes... Fuck me. **[moans]** I want it all. Fuck me with your massive cock while my pathetic slave watches us. Yes. Yes. Deeper.

Look at him, slave. Look how deep he has gotten his dick in my ass. I am so full and stretched out now. I can feel his balls hitting on my well-fucked pussy. Look at you, you're so hard, pet. Turns out you do enjoy watching your Mistress getting fucked by someone else. **[chuckle]** Yes. Yes. **[pleased scream]** You can fuck my ass whenever you want, my bull. Let me feel you deep in my ass while my manwhore watches.

His cock is pounding inside me in a punishing rhythm. You watch mesmerized as it keeps opening me up, stretching me as it pumps in and out, going deeper and deeper with each push. He has bottomed out; he's going to get faster and harder now. And with every thrust of his cock in my ass, you're going to feel your cock growing bigger, and more aroused.

[growl] He's fucking me so deep and hard that you can almost feel it on your own asshole, don't you, you filthy manwhore? My tight little ass was made for him to fuck and you to watch getting fucked. **[moans]** I'm cumming again. I'm—**[scream]** Watch my pussy squirt for a third time. Witness what it's like to be fucked by a real cock.

[panting] Oh yes... Yes... Cum deep inside my asshole you stud. Fill my tight ass deep with your hot seed. My slut is waiting for it. I bet you want to take my bull's cock in you as well. Look how eager you are, look at your cock dripping with precum. **[moans]** Yes. Yes. Shoot that hot load in my asshole. **[gasp]** Yes. Fill me up. Yes. Yes—

[panting more slowly] Ah... That was incredible, wasn't it, slave? I bet you enjoyed every minute of it, even if you think otherwise. You've dreamed of watching me get fucked like that, haven't you? No shame in admitting it.

Now I have a reward for you, since you watched the whole thing. You get to clean me up. That's right. As my bull pulls away from my ass you can see he has filled me with his warm, delicious cum. You get to eat all that now. Isn't that a treat? I move close to you and bend over, bringing my ass and my cunt directly in front of your face. You can see my gaping ass and my wrecked cunt, dripping with cum and my juices. Clean it all up now like a good manwhore.

My bull will leave us now. Thank him before he goes. No, you can have his cock up your ass another time. Would you like that? You can lick my pussy while he fucks. I'm sure you'll love that. But now say goodbye to my bull and focus on your work. Lick all of that cocksauce out of my pussy and my ass.

Press your face between my legs and start licking and sucking my cunt clean. Yes. Yes... That's good. You're working it so well. Lick all of the hot cum dribbling out.

Well done, you little filthy cuck. You've been such a good boy. Now it's time for your final reward. I can feel you ready to burst with arousal and anticipation. Your cock is so hard and red. Watching your Mistress fuck someone else has made you drip like nothing before, huh? I believe you have earned the right to cum. I'm going to do you the honor of jerking you off. That's right. Your Mistress volunteers her hand for your pleasure, loyal slave.

Feel how soft my hand is around your rock-hard cock. You love the feeling of my palm around it even when I'm not moving my hand. Each stroke I give you is bringing you closer and closer to your climax. This one is going to be great, you know? No, my darling pet, I mean it. You have been such a good cuck.

You have become the perfect manwhore. Now... When I count down from five, I want you to cum hard for your Mistress. Five... Feel my palm gently stroking your shaft up and down. Four... It's slow at first but I amp up the speed, jerking you off. Three... My other hand takes a hold of your balls and squeezes them. Two... My hand jerks you off faster and faster, bringing you closer to the final edge. One.... Cum for me now slave, cum for your Mistress's tits. Spread your cum on my beautiful mounds. Watch it drip between the crack slowly, like a pearl necklace.

Yes. That's it. You're such a good cuck. That was a great orgasm, wasn't it? I told you it would be worth it. Now clean up your Mistress's titties with your tongue. Just like that. Well done. That's good. Clean up all the mess you've made. Feel the taste, let it linger on your tongue. That's it. You're such a good boy.

I will now gradually bring you back to your everyday world. Feel how your breaths are returning to a slow and steady rhythm again. I'm so proud of how well you did today. That's right. You will be happier and more relaxed after this, even in the waking world. I know you loved what I did to you today, even if you wouldn't admit it at first...

But it did feel really good, didn't it? **[uncuffs]** You may lay down again if you want. **[uncuffs]** You must be so tired after coming so hard, my pet. Now, close your eyes again and don't open them unless I command you to. When I count down from five, you will begin returning to the waking world. I need you to start seeing yourself back in your safe space. Five... Four... Three... Two... One...

When you hear me snap my fingers, you will wake up at once. Your post-climax elation that's now spreading through your body will relax you even further. Feel the tension leaving you entirely. This feeling will follow you after I snap my fingers, too.

Can't wait to see you again, my sweet, loyal pet. **[snap]**

Erotic Hypnosis Audio Recordings

If you like reading about Erotic Hypnosis, you will LOVE listening to what it sounds like when a real pro reads the scripts.

Hearing my narrator reading those scrips is a seductive treat you can't find anywhere else.

You can get *Erotic Hypnosis: Six Sessions of Guided Femdom Meditation* for free when you sign up for a 30-day Audible trial. Go to my homepage alexandramorris.com to find out how!

"The book is sooo satisfying. It's really worth the buy. Her voice is unbelievably seductive." – Audible listener

"I have listened to many hypnosis / guided meditation audiobooks over the years. I generally get something out of each one, but what I got from this audiobook was a completely mind blowing experience. The first portion of the book is instructional, the latter portion has some sample hypnosis scripts. Whether you are interested in being the hypnotist, or in being hypnotized yourself, this audiobook is a must listen. Put the headphones on and open your mind to the world of erotic hypnosis. You wont regret it." – Audible Listener

Conclusion

Well, that was quite a journey, wasn't it? You might still have misgivings about sexually submitting, and the shame that might emerge from submission is very high on the list. That is entirely normal, and quite frankly, not at all surprising. The back-and-forth between our everyday life roles and what kind of a role we assume in our bedrooms has always been fascinating.

Nowadays, with society being increasingly more tolerant and understanding, personal identity seems to be inherently tied to our sexual expression and vice versa. As a result, men who are or want to explore being submissive in the bedroom, even occasionally, face the dreaded fear of being judged for it. At the end of the day, though, our sexual disposition and our everyday life are not irrevocably tied.

Men, especially cisgender heterosexual men, are brought up with the fear of emasculation (having their "manhood" jeopardized). Although stereotypes have begun to crumble in the past few years, and with toxic masculinity starting to be challenged, the striking majority of men is afraid to experiment in fear of their masculinity being questioned.

Male submissives are usually treated as an outlier on mainstream media because our society has been cultivating a binary culture for at least half a century. There is a toxic and confused conception about what "masculinity" is and how it should be expressed. For decades, masculinity was associated with strength and the subjugation of the opposite sex. Intimidation, objectification, and even degradation of women had come to be associated with the "Alpha male" figure. As a result, behaviors deemed un-masculine, such as being gentle, considerate, or sexually submissive have been seen as deviant. With that, being dominated by a woman is seen as weak or a punchline in a joke. On media especially, sub males have been treated as the butt of a joke for years.

Sub males are often met with confused looks and raised eyebrows, particular if there are "dominant" in other aspects of their lives. Even though things have been steadily improving, it's unfortunate to think of something like the willingness to behave, listen, and please sexually is something to repress and be ashamed of.

As we've seen, there's nothing wrong with submitting. It is absolutely fine to be a man with a softer side. In fact, most male-attracted people will tell you that it's an advantage to be submissive. There's nothing inappropriate about willing and wishing to please people sexually in a consensual relationship. Ultimately, the desire to please can be one of the best qualities in a partner; it doesn't make a man effeminate, as many would believe.

Studies have shown that a woman prefer a man who would rather have her take charge during sex than a partner who is out only for their own satisfaction. There are various factors that explain why a person finds submissive men preferable, but generally speaking, it is thought-provoking to consider what society feels about submissive men. The image of submissive males seems to bother many men; however, plenty of women seem to actually be more attracted to the idea of a man who's willing to surrender his power, whether in the bedroom or in a relationship. That holds especially true if the man in question is usually "Alpha" in other aspects of his life. There is an appeal in strong, confident men who aren't afraid to surrender, not to mention the charm of "breaking down" a strong-willed, buff, and poised man into a willing slave or a "man toy."

Social constructs might have you believe that submitting sexually stems from one being virginal, easily coerced, and having no boundaries. On the contrary, despite the incorrect portrayal of sexual submission on mainstream media, it is something far more collaborative, consensual, and sexy.

As we age, our desires and needs evolve. Getting more comfortable with a partner or with who we frequent makes us more willing to explore our sexuality and kinks, so it isn't strange to suddenly find yourself considering sexual submission for the first time!

Exploring your sexual desires and deepest kinks is very important. It's highly probable that you have heard the trope of the "power boss": people who have been in control and have been making decisions all day, long to unwind by having someone else assuming control (something the media has no trouble depicting). Decision reprieve is not the single reason people enjoy when submissive, though; many people are often aroused by how taboo or "wrong" it feels, or perhaps they are aroused by servicing their partner.

Constantly exploring our desires and needs helps us remain mentally alert and healthy. Submitting can be healing, even spiritual, and by practicing submission in a controlled environment, you can overcome hang-ups and insecurities that might have been constricting you for years. Discovering your kinks and deepest desires can help reinforce self-validation.

There is power in submission. Giving in means you are pursuing your desires without fear while subverting patriarchal stereotypes. People don't grasp that the submissive is also often the one in power, as he is the object of desire and the center of attention in a scene. Some submissive men actually feel more powerful when they look up at the dominant woman or partner they are pleasing.

The scripts and sessions in this book provide a superb tool for you to find yourself and rejuvenate your sexuality in the safety of your own home before exploring your submissive side even further. They are specifically designed to do away with all the ideas that constrict you from finding who you truly are as a sexual being. Shameful thoughts and associations that keep you in place will be stripped away, making way for a better, more confident version of yourself. You might even find yourself being more effusive and comfortable, as traits you have been repressing for a long time will finally be allowed to emerge.

Even if you consider erotic hypnosis weird or unconventional, all that matters is that the methods work, as you will hopefully soon find out yourself! It isn't me or my scripts that bring out the best results possible, it's your subconscious that holds the power to do this.

It's all you.

Life is far too short to be ashamed of the healthy, consensual sex we want to have.

Happy playing!

Connect With Me

There are millions of books online, and I'm glad that you discovered this one and got to the end.

Thank you for that!

What I hate after reading a book is the feeling that it's stuffed with bad (and boring) content that is easily available on Wikipedia and random blogs.

If I gave you that, I deserve to know that.

On the other hand, if I gave you what you expected (or more), I would like to know that. Tell me in the reviews. The experts say I'm supposed to insert a link here and beg for a review, but I'm not going to that. You know how to leave one if you want.

If you liked this book and want more, don't forget to listen to how erotic hypnosis sounds when a pro reads the scrips!

Enjoy.

Alexandra Morris

www.alexandramorris.com

Milton Keynes UK
Ingram Content Group UK Ltd.
UKHW010814271123
433341UK00008B/764